The Extraordinary Case
of Sister Liguori

Dedication

To my family, past, present and future

This is for my husband, Charlie, my children, Catherine, Jennifer, Michael, Paula and Clare and my grandchildren, Annie, Jack, Ryan, Leona, Olivia, Emma and Alicia, for their unconditional love.

The Extraordinary Case

of

Sister Liguori

Maureen McKeown

Leo Press

First published in 2017 by Leo Press, 38 Old Course Road,
Downpatrick, Co Down, BT30 8BD
www.theextraordinarycaseofsisterliguori.com

British Library Cataloguing in Publication Data
A catalogue record for this book is available from
the British Library

ISBN 978-0-9955775-0-3

Typeset by Amolibros, Milverton, Somerset
www.amolibros.com
This book production has been managed by Amolibros
Printed and bound by T J International Ltd, Padstow,
Cornwall, UK

Acknowledgements

First, I have to thank those who keep records of our past allowing access to online historical documents and newspaper accounts. I relied heavily on the trove of headline material available in past copies of The *Sydney Morning Herald* and The Wagga *Daily Express*, although all newspapers throughout Australia and New Zealand deserve a thank you. I also thank ancestry.com for their part in providing much information.

I was inspired to write this book by articles penned by Jeff Kildea, Adjunct Professor in Irish Studies at UNSW ('Where Crows Gather*)*. Also, Les Hetherington, Post-Graduate Researcher at the Australian University's National Centre of Biography ('The Escaped Nun Sister Liguori and Australian Sectarianism after the First World War'). Also, Charles Sturt University Regional Archives, Wagga Wagga ('Nun in a Nightgown'). I thank you all.

I could never forget the welcome I received from the Sisters of the Presentation of the Blessed Virgin Mary, both in Kildare and in Wagga Wagga. Sister Alexis Horsley, Archivist in Mount Erin Convent, gave willingly of her time and provided helpful information when I visited Australia. Sister Alexis also arranged for me to visit Father Peter Morrissey who had attended Brigid Partridge in her later years. Again, thank you.

I also wish to thank June Considine aka Laura Elliot, Author, Patricia O'Reilly, Author, Dianne Ascroft, Author, along with all members of The Historical Novel Society, whose advice and encouragement was never far away. A mention also goes to Michael McLaughlin who designed my website:
www.theextraordinarycaseofsisterliguori.com

My thanks also go to Hilary Johnson, Literary Agent, for polishing up my manuscript before placing it into the professional hands of Jane Tatam of Amolibros who excelled in bringing my book to print, helping me realize my dream. Jane expertly chose Tony Denton who did an outstanding job designing the front cover.

To everyone who played a part in helping to produce the book you now hold in your hand, I say a big thank you. Finally, I thank you, the reader.

About the author, Maureen McKeown

Maureen McKeown was born in Berkshire, England. She was educated by Sisters of Mercy at St John Bosco Primary School in Woodley, near Reading. At the age of eleven she moved to Northern Ireland with her family and was a boarder at St Joseph's Convent Grammar School in Donaghmore, Co Tyrone. She has great admiration for the wonderful work of nuns and holds the warmest memories of their guidance. She went on to study at the Belfast College of Business Studies and began her working life in the NI Civil Service in Parliament Buildings, Stormont, as a Personal Secretary. It was a 'troubled time' for Northern Ireland as a campaign for Civil Rights heightened sectarianism and precipitated more than thirty years of bloodshed.

Maureen's parents moved to Downpatrick, Co Down, in 1973 and a short time later, she met Charlie, her husband of thirty-seven years. Maureen quit the Civil Service to raise five children, during which time she also helped with the administration and running of the business Charlie and herself set up nearly forty years ago.

She had little time for hobbies but when her family flew the nest, she turned to the Internet to research her ancestors. The computer screen flashed up information on her Great Aunt, Brigid Partridge, and she was fascinated with what she read. It was the beginning of her writing journey. Research took her to the presentation convent that Brigid entered in Kildare, Ireland, at the age of seventeen. The warm and friendly welcome extended to her from the community of sisters gave Maureen the desire to pursue Brigid's story further and she travelled to Australia where she received the same warm and friendly welcome from the Sisters of the Presentation of the Blessed Virgin

Mary in Wagga Wagga. Sister Alexis, the Archivist, gave freely of her time in showing her around the convent and contributing helpful material. When Maureen returned from Australia, she painstakingly sifted through a mountain of information and carefully crafted the remarkable true story of her great aunt. *The Extraordinary Case of Sister Liguori* would help her through her darkest hours after being diagnosed with Motor Neurone Disease/ALS in 2015.

This is her first book.

Note from author

This is a true story written in narrative non-fiction style. I have tried to stick to the facts as far as possible, but a few characters and scenes have been introduced for the purpose of relating the story, along with personal gestures and internal thoughts. All speech is taken directly or adapted from contemporary historical accounts.

Maureen McKeown
June 2017

Chapter One

Mama is seated in the pony and trap at the front gate, her eyes glinting with pride. The cart shifts a little when Dada helps me up with my suitcase and Ben, the brown cob, kicks at the ground restless to be away. My young brother jumps in quickly and Dada follows, tucking a woollen blanket about our knees. I look to our stone cottage nesting in a hollow beside several tall oak trees where my three sisters are huddling in the doorway, their eyes red and puffy.

'We'll miss you, Bride,' they call out, hoping in their hearts that somehow I will change my mind. 'Sure I'm only going down the road,' I shout back and Mama clasps my hand trying to soothe the pain of parting. The driver steers the cart towards Brownstown crossroads and, with a gentle flick of the reins, Ben picks up speed where the wooden signpost, blackened and pitted with age, says *Kildare 11 miles*. A steady trot takes us along the grassy verges of The Curragh where cows and sheep graze freely on thousands of acres of lush unfenced grassland in the heart of County Kildare. The fresh breeze awakens my senses to the Irish countryside that is set ablaze with ever-changing colours. Often compared to a large green tapestry, it is tinged with the orange glow of an early sunrise. Clusters of bright yellow furze bushes are growing in abundance far across the open lands, to the distant heather-covered Wicklow Mountains. As summer fades into autumn in 1908 a new season is marked, so too is a new beginning in my life.

When I announced my decision to enter an enclosed convent, Mama could not hide her delight telling me it was the proper life to lead. Dada was not so happy, arguing it was unnatural for a group of women to be locked away from the world, praying, fasting and doing penance. He said my head was filled with religious nonsense and that sacrificing my life in this way would be far from easy. He asked me what did I know of the world? 'Nothing,' he answered, not letting me speak, 'because your mother protects you from everything … from the very wind blowing on your face.'

'But, Dada, I want to be a teacher and this is my chance.'

'How do you know what you want, Brigid? You are only seventeen.'

Mama helped me win the argument, telling him the matter was already settled.

We reach the town of Kildare, and turn left on to the aptly named Convent Road. The driver guides Ben skilfully up the slight incline and through the gates of St Brigid's Convent, bringing the cart to a halt at the main entrance. Dada rings the bell. The heavy metal door opens slowly and an elderly nun, her sizeable headdress covering most of her face, invites us into the front parlour. Furnished with upholstered chairs and a bookcase filled with religious books, a piano is set into a corner and Holy pictures adorn the walls. A long sash window looks onto the front gardens where the large beech trees will soon be stripped of their glossy leaves.

We are left alone in the cold, musty room where the sickly smell of polish plucks at our throats. Mama pulls me to her with a sense of urgency, her tear-stained face dampening mine. 'I will pray that God keeps you strong.'

'Please, Mama, don't fret, I am not far away and I'll write as often as I am allowed.'

Jody's small arms are around my waist squeezing me tight and his young face, bearing early signs of striking good looks, seeks solace from me. 'Who is going to look after me when you're gone, Bride?'

'You're a big man, Jody, even at eleven years old. It is your turn now to take care of the family.'

Dada kisses the top of my head. 'Is this what you truly want, Bride?'

'Yes, Dada, it is.' Calling me Bride assures me of his blessing.

His steel grey eyes mist over and I cannot hold onto my tears any longer. Suddenly, we are all crying.

The Reverend Mother enters the parlour telling my family it is time for them to leave. 'Sister Mary Brigid is now in God's hands as she surrenders herself into His service.' The door closes heavily. I am locked in and the world is locked out.

Within a few short weeks I learn I cannot remain in an enclosed convent near my family, for the possibility of seeing them might harm my vocation. I write to Mama telling her I am to be sent to a convent in Australia where teaching nuns are needed.

My journey begins two days before Christmas. The ground is white with snow and the beech trees are settled into winter's sleep. When they wake in spring, I will be far away. I travel to a convent in Dublin where I meet three members of the Presentation Order of the Blessed Virgin Mary, two fully professed nuns and a young postulant, like myself, who will travel with me to Australia. We board the overnight boat to Liverpool on Christmas Eve and continue to London by train. We arrive cold and tired at Tilbury Docks on a frosty Christmas morning with snowflakes swirling from a darkening sky. My long hair, tied back into ringlets, is pinned beneath a black cap and I turn up the collar of my coat to ward off the icy wind blowing at my back from across the River Thames. Cleared by a doctor of carrying contagious diseases on board we are allowed to embark *SS Oroya*. The two older nuns remain on the upper deck while Annie and I are dismissed to a cabin in the lower part of the ship where two metal beds are fixed one above the other. Annie claims the bottom bunk while I climb up to the top, squeezing my long body into the meagre space beneath the low-timbered ceiling. I set my black woollen coat over the thin blanket for extra warmth.

By the end of December we have reached Gibraltar and *The Oroya* docks to take rations on board. Allowed ashore with our travelling companions, we stay close to the ship welcoming the feel of dry land beneath our feet and the tingle of warm air on our cheeks. Journeying on through the month of January, we pass the Bay of Naples in Italy, past Sicily and then Crete. We have little to do on board, except quietly pray and read religious books. The continual rocking of the ship on water causes a great deal of sickness as it sails on through the Suez Canal, the Red Sea, across the Arabian Sea and over the Indian Ocean. Confined to bed in the small, airless cabin, I long for the comfort of Mama's arms. In early February, the deep blue sea becomes a lighter shade, a sign we are nearing land.

★★★

B rigid, Brigid, quickly … wake up … come and see Australia!' Annie's words nudge me awake and I open my eyes to golden sunshine. 'We will be docking soon,' she says, unable to hide her excitement.

Yawning, I stretch my long limbs in the cramped space of my berth. 'We have spent forty-three days at sea, Annie, I have counted every one of them.' A grating sound vibrates through the ship and the engines judder to a halt as I pack my few belongings into the suitcase that has travelled so far with me. We make our way to the top deck, shading our eyes from the strong glare of the sun. As *SS Oroya* idles towards the shore, we strain to catch our first glimpse of Australia. The tallest buildings we have ever seen shimmer on the horizon. The crew works hard guiding the vessel into its moorings and secures it firmly before the passengers file down the gangway like an army of ants. On Saturday, 6 February 1909, I stand spellbound by the chaos on Sydney Circular Quay as Annie and I wait with the two older nuns. Our heavy religious clothing is not fitting in such high temperatures and we attract strange looks from passers-by.

'Have they never seen a nun before? They should show some respect,' one of the older nuns snaps, indignant at being the object of fascination.

Several priests walk towards us and I learn two of them will escort me to my designated convent. I say a rushed goodbye to Annie and thank the older nuns. The journey continues by train and a gentle breeze blows through the window as it chugs across the farmlands of New South Wales bringing a little relief from the fiery heat.

'Look, look … there's a kangaroo,' one of the priests says as he points to the strange sight of a brown marsupial hopping around in the shade of a large gum tree. The priests have fun outsmarting each other naming the animals and birds we spot. We see koalas and cockatoos painted like rainbows. 'We have birds that sound like monkeys, but it's the snakes and spiders you have to watch out for,' one of them warns.

'St Patrick banished all the snakes in Ireland,' I tell them, shyly.

I am a stranger to this country. Comparing the vast open stretches of golden land to the green fields I have left behind is painful. Dusty towns and wide streets with wooden-framed buildings and open verandahs replace the narrow lanes and whitewashed stone cottages of Ireland. The trees here have large branches that spread outwards, like parasols, giving shade from the melting sun. The trees at home have branches bent inwards by the wind and rain, like battered umbrellas.

★★★

The final part of the journey is by coach and when we reach our destination, the convent bus is waiting to take us the two miles out of town. 'Wagga Wagga, the place of many crows - it is often shortened to Wagga,' one of the priests muses. It is early evening when we turn up the driveway and I see Mount Erin for the first time through the trees. The majestic red-bricked Tudor-style building with rounded towers and wide verandahs stands resplendent, ringed in a halo of sunlight from the dipping sun. I am overcome at the line of waving nuns gathered on the granite steps, sweltering in the heat of their habits, awaiting my arrival from Ireland.

The priests are taken for something to eat while I report to the office where the Reverend Mother is waiting to talk to me. 'I am Mother Stanislaus. We are delighted you have arrived safely from Ireland to join our community here in Mount Erin,' she smiles. 'Have you brought your Baptismal Certificate with you?'

'Yes, Mother. I also have a letter from my Parish Priest in Newbridge,' I answer, my voice reflecting around me in the high-ceilinged room.

Brigid Mary Partridge was born on 19th October 1890 in Newbridge, Kildare, and was baptized into the Roman Catholic faith in St Conleth's Church the following week. She is the second oldest in a family of five. Her father is a serving British soldier at the Curragh Army Camp here in Kildare. Although he was born an English Protestant, he converted to the Catholic faith on his marriage to Brigid's mother, Anne, a devout Irish Catholic. Brigid has the benefit of a full Catholic education. I have known the family for many years, and can attest to Brigid's excellent character. She is quiet and reserved and I believe she has the strength to persevere in religion to the end of her life.

The Reverend Mother's face, partially hidden behind her headdress, tells me little, but her manner is kind. Her thin frame is lost among the layers of her habit. Large wooden rosary beads and a bunch of keys are attached to the black leather belt around her waist. On the wall behind her hangs a portrait bearing the inscription Nano Nagle, Foundress of the Presentation Order of the Blessed Virgin Mary whose mission began in Ireland during Penal times when Catholics were stripped of their religion and education. As a saviour for the suffering poor, her work spread to other countries and many single educated women aspired to join her. Mother Stanislaus is one of the original five pioneering nuns who arrived from Ireland in 1874 to help establish a convent and schools for the Christian education of the children of the early settlers in Wagga, many of whom were Irish fleeing the oppression of their own native land.

'You will have a fortnight's rest after your long journey, during which time you will become acquainted with the daily routine of the convent by taking part in prayers, meals and light duties along with the other postulants.' Mother Stanislaus has a lilting Kildare accent like Mama. She rings a bell to call one of the sisters. 'Sister Angela will take you to the refectory for something to eat. She will show you around the convent, after which you will have half an hour's recreation when the sisters do their mending.' As we make our way to the chapel for prayers, the convent is untroubled. The only sounds breaking through the tranquillity are the sweet chants of the sisters intoning the psalms. At eight o'clock I am taken to the community room and given a place beside another postulant.

A sudden rush of chat and laughter brings the convent to life. The young girl beside me introduces herself. 'Hello, I'm Eileen Hayes.'

'Hello,' I answer quietly.

'There is no need to whisper. This is our recreation. We talk while we sew,' she says, handing me a threadbare habit to patch.

'Thank you, Eileen, I'm Brigid Partridge.'

'I saw you arriving from Ireland earlier today,' she says.

A young girl sits down on my right. 'I entered today, too. My name is Mary Fitzpatrick. I'm Australian.'

'For a glorious half an hour every night we can talk! I want to hear your Irish accent so, come on, let's make the most of it!' Eileen urges, begging Mary and me for news. 'We are not told anything that's going on outside these walls.'

Eileen says our places in the convent are fixed between the postulant who entered before and the postulant who entered after. When the bell hails the end of recreation, Eileen leads the way, I follow and Mary comes behind as we file to the chapel for night prayers. The Great Silence begins at nine o'clock and is observed throughout the night until after breakfast every morning. I again take my place among the postulants at bedtime where a sister stands over us in the dormitory, rigid as a statue, holding a forefinger pressed tightly to her lips as we wash and undress. When I lie down on the narrow metal bed, I close my eyes and within minutes my mind is journeying back to Ireland of its own free will.

Chapter Two

On Sunday, 21 February 1909, I am formally accepted as a member of the Presentation Order of the Blessed Virgin Mary. It is the beginning of my commitment to God to do His work and lead a purely spiritual life. I will belong body and soul to the service of this community.

The Mistress of Novices, Sister Clare, will take charge of my vocational training and I am placed in her care. She gives me a booklet on the regulations governing enclosed life that I must learn by heart, keeping it about my person and observing the rules at all times. She instructs me to follow her to join the other postulants and from that moment I learn to walk through the cloisters in complete silence, with downcast eyes and short measured steps.

Sister Clare's small, round figure with plump cheeks stands before us. She writes the horarium on to a blackboard, and, through a thin, pinched mouth, says, 'This is your hourly timetable. It is to be followed at all times. If you are in the middle of something, you immediately abandon it.' The day is set out from five a.m.: rise, to ten p.m.: bed. Continuous prayers and fasting along with cleaning duties will dominate my life during my six months as a postulant. I will then receive the habit and white veil of the order and given a new name in religion. When I am professed I will be a teacher.

I must become like clay in the hands of a potter, to be moulded by my superiors as they wish.

To avoid damaging our religious progress, postulants are separated from novices, who are separated from the professed nuns. Choir nuns – teaching nuns – are separated from the lay nuns who do the general housework and cleaning. I pity the gaunt outlines of the ageing lay nuns, held in lesser regard than the choir nuns. They have little education and usually come from a family background that cannot provide a dowry. Their lives are taken up with housework and menial tasks. Their bodies, bent and stooped over buckets of steaming water, line the lengthy corridors on their knees, swirling steaming cloths over the vast floors with their habits pinned up behind them. They rest occasionally to wipe the sweat trickling from their brows. I try not to think what growing old in this community will be like.

The convent is controlled by a system of bells. Obeying the bell is obeying the voice of God. Each morning, I fall from a warm bed on to cold floorboards when the calling bell rings. Dressing quickly, I get into line behind Eileen. Only the faint sound of birdsong disturbs the meditative silence as I kneel before the altar, rubbing sleep from my eyes. Three more hours will pass before we eat.

I long for a letter from home and at last Sister Clare calls my name. She removes the letter from its envelope and the air is scented with lavender, bringing me a clear image of Mama walking into Newbridge with it tucked safely into the cane basket she always carries. Her first stop will be J. H. Clinton's on the main street for groceries and a bottle of whiskey for Dada. She will then go to the Post Office. Her eyes, as blue as cornflowers, brightening with pleasure when she asks for the special stamps needed to post it, telling the postmistress she is writing to her daughter, a nun in Australia, knowing it will be repeated throughout the day to every customer who passes through the door.

'You're quiet tonight, Brigid. Are you all right?' Eileen asks later at recreation.

'I received a letter from my family and expected it to be filled with news of my sisters and brother. I longed to hear words of comfort and strained to hear more but there was no more. When Sister Clare read it to me, it contained a few simple lines. With a wily stare, she secreted it to the folds of her habit, without a thought or care for the yearning within me.'

'Our letters are censored by the Mother Superior before they are read to us,' Mary says, 'in case they contain something offensive to our vocation.'

What could Mama have written that would offend anybody?

'I sought permission to reply and, as soon as I had finished, it was snatched from my hand and ripped into small pieces.'

'What on earth did you write?' Eileen and Mary ask.

'I told them the food was served cold and there was never enough. Sister Clare made me sit down to write a proper letter telling my parents how content I am.'

'Sadly, one of the Rules is – Thou shalt not complain,' Mary says lightheartedly. 'The nuns could have trouble with you, Brigid Partridge.'

★★★

We are busy sewing our new religious garments in preparation for receiving our white veils, and spend our final week as postulants in retreat in total silence studying the rules of the order. Although I will not be under vows until I am professed, I must live as though I am. The vow of poverty means I will own nothing. Everything is owned in common with the community. I will be given food and clothing according to necessity.

The next vow is the promise of absolute and unquestioning obedience to my superiors and to the rules of the Order. I will sacrifice my judgement, reason and conscience and I must obey the Mother Superior as holding her authority from God.

The third vow is chastity. The person of a sister is considered sacred and holy. I must subdue my flesh by fasting and abstinence as far as my health will permit. At table, I must eat what is set before me, or go without, only taking food to strengthen my body for the performance of my duties.

We will cast off everything worldly, including our names and we are eager to learn the new religious names we will be given. On the day of the ceremony, a stream of sunshine reflects off the stained glass window spraying a rainbow of colours over the oratory and Mother Stanislaus says, 'it is a blessing from God'. The postulants, dressed like brides, stand before the altar. The choir sings '*O Gloriosa Virginum*' before Mass is celebrated by the Bishop of Goulburn, with Father Mullins assisting. When Mass ends, the Bishop gives a blessing, quoting a text from St Matthew:

> *And everyone that hath left house, or brethren, or sisters, or father, or mother, or wife, or children, or lands, for my name's sake, shall receive a hundredfold and shall possess life everlasting. You have chosen to embrace evangelical poverty and are abandoning everything worldly to follow Christ,' he says. 'I trust that you will persevere in your constancy and endeavour to adorn your soul with the many priceless gifts of God. The life which you are about to enter will enable you to hold conversations with God on most important subjects and a far greater friendship will be cemented between Him and you.*

The Bishop asks each of us, 'My child, what do you demand?'

'The mercy of God, the holy habit of religion, the charity of the order and the society of the mothers and sisters,' I answer.

'Is it with your own free will and consent you demand the holy habit of religion?'

'Yes, My Lord.'

'My child, do you think you have sufficient strength to bear constantly the sweet yoke of our Lord Jesus Christ for the love and fear of God alone to the end of your life?'

'Relying on the mercy of God and on the prayers of the mothers and sisters, I hope to be able to do so.'

'What God has commenced in you may He perfect.'

Each postulant returns to her cell that has been scrupulously cleaned for the next stage of the ceremony.

While I wait for Mother Stanislaus, I unfurl my long plaits from their ribbons letting my hair tumble loose down my back. Since I was a child, I loved the feel of it. For a moment, I play with it, curling it around my fingers and think of Mama washing it and combing out the tangles while I dried it beside the fire in the kitchen. Mother

Stanislaus appears. Neither a heartening word, nor a smile slips from her unbending stance. She holds a large pair of scissors in her hand and snaps them open, their razor-sharp blades pointing towards me. With a glaring, cold stare she forces me to turn towards the wall. To be embraced in this new world, I must become dead to the old world and it is now time for part of my real self to be severed. I shut my eyes as she presses her palm down hard on the top of my head, yanking it back. With an unsteady rush of breath, she begins cutting. Chop. Chop. Chop. The scissors rest and opening my eyes, I strain to stop my hands from flying up to my head to feel my ragged scalp, bereft of the thick, healthy curls now lying at my feet. With no time to grieve, I am ordered to cast off my white dress and fold it neatly away before being buried in the over-sized black habit that is pulled down over me. A starched white cap is clamped tightly to my shorn head and a long white veil is attached to it with pins. The weight of the robe restricts my movement as I return to the chapel for the blessing of the habit.

We are ushered to prostrate ourselves on the bare floor and I strain to breathe as I renounce the world and forsake my worldly name.

'Receive, *Sister Mary Liguori*, the white veil, the emblem of inward purity, that thou mayest follow the Lamb without stain, and mayest walk with Him in white. In the name of the Father, and of the Son, and of the Holy Ghost.'

'Amen,' I answer, remaining prostrate.

The refrain *Regnum mundi* is sung by one of the nuns as the novices reply along with the choir: 'My heart hath uttered a good work, I speak my works to the King.' The *Veni Creator* is intoned by the Bishop and, after more prayers, each novice is sprinkled with holy water. As I rise from the floor, a silver cross is placed around my neck, and a silver ring on my left hand, symbolizing my marriage to Jesus Christ. The choir sings the hymn *Deus misereatur*. With my long habit rustling around me, I embrace my fellow sisters. Eileen Hayes will be Sister Mary Raphael and Mary Fitzpatrick will be Sister Mary Kostka.

We are each presented with a copy of the writings of the Saints whose names we have been given, that we will imitate their holy lives. I am given *The True Spouse of Christ* by Alphonsus Liguori.

Afterwards, we gather for a celebratory meal in the refectory along with the invited guests. I sit alone watching the new novices enjoy this special occasion with their families and think of how proud my family, especially Mama, would have been attending this sacred ceremony today. Their absence from such a significant moment in my life makes me realize for the first time since entering the convent how isolated I am from what matters most to me.

Chapter Three

I continue as a novice for two and a half years, preparing to take temporary vows and receive the black veil. On Tuesday, 26 September 1911, guests are seated in St Eugene's chapel and sanctuary, which is decorated with lilies of the valley and lighted candles. His Lordship, Dr Gallagher, Bishop of Goulburn, who is attended by the Right Reverend Monsignor Buckley and the Reverend Fathers Mulligan and Shannon, addresses the congregation:

> *The occasion of this religious ceremony is the reception and profession of a number of young ladies who have decided on the adoption of the life of a religieuse, and are giving up the affairs of everyday life to enter the cloister of the convent, there to devote their energies and their talents to the teaching of the young.*

Later, Mother Stanislaus summons me to her office. 'It is our life's mission to produce young Catholics who are knowledgeable about their faith. There is a shortage of teachers at St Joseph's in Lockhart. The school opened its doors three years ago to sixteen boys and twelve girls. By the end of the first year, numbers had grown to over two hundred, increasing every year since. Sister Clare has put your name forward to take classes.' My smile broadens as she assigns me to teach catechism to the younger children. 'Your teaching duties will begin tomorrow morning, Sister. I know your mother and father could not attend today's ceremony,' she says, holding out an unopened envelope. 'This letter arrived earlier from them.' I am barely able to fight a childish urge to jump up and down with joy. I place it in the pocket of my new habit until later.

Back in my cell, I retrieve it instantly, before carefully folding my new religious garments. I wash, put on my nightgown and dip my fingers into holy water before kneeling down to thank God for the wondrous day. In bed, I open the envelope with such care as not to tear any part of it. Snuggling down, I am blessed with a rare moment of happiness alone with my family.

Brownstown
Kildare
Ireland
15 August 1911

Dearest Bride

How quickly three years have passed. We are filled with pride in the young girl who travelled so far from her home to devote herself to God and lead the proper life in a convent. Your father worries you may be lonely and hopes you have overcome some of your shyness. He compares your life in the convent to his life in the army, saying it will be Rules! Rules! Rules! I am sure it is not like that.

I am happy to tell you that Joseph is studying to become a priest and Lizzie has written to a French order of nuns whom she hopes to join. Susan is teaching and Kathleen now helps me at home. The Curragh army camp is expanding and construction workers are flooding into the area. Newbridge is bustling with the extra business and we are taking in boarders. They are a mixed selection of gentlemen from Ireland and England. We have an English actor, Mr Russell, who keeps us entertained in the evenings.

Sometimes there are visiting priests from Australia at Mass and I wait afterwards to tell them about you. I have asked them to pay you a visit if they are passing Mount Erin Convent.

*Do you get visitors? We remember you every night when we
pray the Rosary together. Please keep us in your prayers.*

Your loving family in Ireland

I read the letter again, fold it back into its envelope and place it
under my pillow. I want to shout my own good news – tomorrow I
am going to be a teacher.

★★★

I wake early. Mother Superior will check my appearance and I pay
special attention to my hands and nails, scrubbing them until they
almost bleed. I worry at the scant preparation I have received for
the task ahead. Sister Kostka and Sister Raphael have assured me I
will learn from the other teaching sisters as I go along.

I have not ventured beyond Mount Erin since my arrival in
Australia and have forgotten the colonial-style buildings flanking
the wide, dusty streets as I travel through Wagga in the black cab. I
am dizzy with excitement as I look up at a cloudless blue sky.

Sister Mary Philomena welcomes me, along with Sister Mary
Josephine and Sister Gerard. The large, bright classroom is divided
by a partition. Pictures cover the walls and a large clock is mounted
above the blackboard. 'You must instil orderly and modest behaviour
into their minds as well as obedience to the teachers,' Sister Mary
Philomena instructs.

The children rise from their seats. 'Good morning, Sister
Philomena.'

'This is your new teacher, Sister Mary Liguori.'

'Good morning Sister Mary Lig … Ligoor.' The children giggle.

Sister Philomena tells me to write my name on the board before
leaving me alone in front of a class of at least forty children.
The desks are set in pairs. The girls, their hair tied up in ribbons,
wear long smocks that cover their ankles. The young boys wear
short trousers and leather boots more suited to the rural areas
they come from. Lifting the stick of chalk, dust sprays down my

sleeve as I spell out my name: S I S T E R M A R Y L I G U O R I. 'Now, who is going to tell me what you do every morning when you get up?'

'Sister, Sister!'

'I will answer if you call me by my proper name.'

'Sister Ligwori!' one little boy shouts.

'What's your name?'

'Christopher, Sister Ligwori.' A wave of blond curly hair falls over his eye. 'I get out of bed!'

Taking a moment, I let the laughter die out.

'What else do you do, Christopher?'

'I make the sign of the cross and say my prayers.'

'Good boy.'

Most of the children live on local farms, helping out with early-morning chores before school. With overcrowded classes, some days are easier than others. Gaining confidence, I teach the children their catechism and the commandments. They learn to honour and respect their parents and how to examine their consciences every night before going to bed. They are also prepared for First Confession and First Holy Communion.

After six months, I am transferred to St Brendan's School at Ganmain. The school opened five years ago and, as the numbers grow, so does the demand for teachers. Lessons are conducted in the original church building beside the convent where I stay with a small community of nuns during term time. Classes cover all levels of education, but I continue teaching the younger pupils. I tingle with delight when their young trusting faces look to me for inspiration. My training as a teacher comes as guidance from Sister Mary Columba and Sister Mary Vincent.

Towards the end of 1914, I am admitted to Lewisham Hospital in Sydney to undergo a nasal operation. It is my first taste of freedom in six years and I am able to catch up with the world through the newspapers. We had been told in the convent that England had declared war on Germany on 22 August 1914. Every day I witness the arrival of wounded soldiers at the hospital and see first hand the savagery of war. My spell in hospital also affords me the opportunity of writing home without my letters being inspected, the matron offering to post them for me. I write to each of my sisters and to Jody and I write to Mama and Dada, assuring them that I am recovering well and asking them not to mention receiving letters from me. When I leave Lewisham Hospital I convalesce in Mount Erin before returning to Ganmain for a further three years during which time I take my final vows that I am bound to forever.

★★★

I go back to Mount Erin in February 1918. Mother Mary Aloysius now holds the office of Mother Superior and she assigns me to take a class of forty young boys in the infant department of St Mary's for an hour and a half each day for religious instruction.

'I cannot believe there is so much work involved in teaching boys who look so angelic with their curly hair, innocent eyes and freckled faces and how suddenly they can become so spirited! I hope they behave tomorrow during the diocesan inspection,' I confide to Sister Raphael at recreation.

'Don't yell at them in front of the inspector. Use your eyes … like this.' She flashes a severe look that makes me laugh.

'It is so good to be back at Mount Erin!'

The following morning, I present myself to Mother Aloysius after breakfast. Pain is burning a path through my stomach and I try to stay steady, holding out my hands for examination as the floor sways beneath me. I am thankful to be dismissed quickly with an impatient wag of the finger.

'You look awful – are you sick?' Sister Kostka whispers behind me as I stagger to the lavatory. Today of all days! Dragging myself through the playground, I breathe in slowly, hoping the fresh air will relieve the spasms shooting through my abdomen. Circling the classroom is a whirlwind of noise and I quicken my pace to find Mother Aloysius standing in front of the class demanding immediate silence, her face telling me of her disapproval. The diocesan inspector is already seated at the back of the classroom and observes me questioning the children on their catechism until the bell finally rings at eleven o'clock.

I walk to the refectory, sitting in silence between Sister Raphael and Sister Kostka. I play with the bowl of soup set before me and a crust of congealed fat floats to the surface. I rush from the refectory, my stomach retching, holding a handkerchief over my mouth.

'Are you any better?' Sister Kostka asks later at recreation.

'I won't feel better until I'm in bed,' I tell her, stifling a yawn. 'I am glad the inspection is over. It's been a long day and the boys were playing up a little.'

'Mother Superior has been stirring us up all week. Look around – the convent and school are polished to such a degree that even the spiders have left,' Sister Raphael says playfully.

'What would I do without you to lift my spirits? Hopefully that will be the end of it.'

Mother Aloysius calls me to her office the following night and I am late for recreation.

'We thought you weren't coming. You're very pale. Is everything all right?' Sister Kostka asks.

'I was with Mother Aloysius. She told me that I was unable to keep control in the classroom and she was not happy with me.'

'Did you tell her you weren't feeling well?'

'She wouldn't listen. She severely reprimanded me, saying I knew we were having an inspection. She proceeded to tell me that the organization and running of a large convent such as Mount Erin is dependent on each of us playing our part. Then she fell silent and I could hear the clock ticking as she took her time to continue. I wondered why she couldn't just say what she had planned for me. Finally, she took pleasure in telling me that due to a shortage of lay nuns, she is temporarily relieving me of teaching duties and putting me in charge of the refectory.'

'Oh, no! Every sister dreads the work in the refectory!' Sister Kostka says.

'Yes, I know. It will be for a fortnight while they await the arrival of a young lay nun to replace me. I will then return to my teaching post. Her exact words were, "You will receive this office as coming from the Lord. You will perform it with great care. Your daily religious obligations will be less than usual so your tasks can be accomplished."'

'How do you feel about it?' Sister Kostka asks sympathetically.

'It is humiliating in front of the whole community!'

'A fortnight isn't long,' Sister Raphael consoles.

★★★

The following morning, the usual prayers and devotion fill the three hours before breakfast after which I remain in the refectory to take up my new duties. Sister Gertrude gives me a white apron to cover my habit along with a timetable setting out the day. The list is endless: clearing tables, washing-up, drying-up, brushing and polishing the floors, answering calls at the door and preparing the table for twenty teaching nuns coming in at eleven o'clock. Yesterday, I was one of these nuns filing silently into the room, inclining to the great crucifix that hangs above the head table. Sister Raphael and Sister Kostka throw me a pitying look and I blink a greeting back. While they are lunching, I have playground duties for fifteen minutes and I rush out to mind the younger children of St Mary's.

A gentle tug at my sleeve draws my attention to a wide-eyed little boy standing beside me. 'Will you be here to look after us tomorrow, Sister Liguori?'

'I don't know. Do you want me to look after you tomorrow?'

'Yes, please, Sister. You make us laugh when you pull funny faces.'

'Do you mean like this?' I twist my face and hear his giggles as he runs after the other children.

When I return to the refectory I am told the names of the nuns who will be taking dinner and I lay the tables. When all the nuns are seated, I carry the vegetables from the kitchen, and after that the puddings. Again, I am occupied in washing-up. The day continues with more prayers, devotion and a light meal which I have to quickly clear away to allow me to enjoy my half-hour's recreation, after which there are night prayers and then, finally, I go to bed at ten p.m.

Every day is the same. Staggering under pots of steaming water, I carry them from the stove to the deep enamel sink in the kitchen. I clear the tables of plates and cutlery and pile them on to the draining board. My glasses cloud over when I immerse my hands into the boiling water. Crimson marks weave a pattern across my skin and as soon as I remove them from the steaming liquid, Sister Gertrude forces a sweeping brush at me.

'This is how to sweep the floor. Hold the brush firmly. The refectory must be cleaned and ready for inspection by Mother Aloysius. Do not leave a corner of this room untouched,' she orders.

When I finish sweeping, I roll up my sleeves, tuck my habit into the black belt around my waist and kneel down. I scrub and polish the refectory floor with a heavy brush and cloths; the strong detergents clog my nose and throat. Other duties take me from the refectory and I return to a sink overflowing with dishes. When I finish clearing the last of the plates I sit down at 3.30 p.m. to a meagre portion of cold, watery soup. I discard a lump of fatty gristle and push the bowl aside. Sister Gertrude pushes it back towards me.

'You must eat what is set before you, Sister.'

I spoon the lump of glistening fat into my mouth, the putrid smell seeping through my nostrils as I chew. Slimy grease dribbles down my chin and I force myself to swallow it.

'Now, Liguori, you can wash up your bowl and cutlery.'

Sister Agatha enters the refectory. 'I notice you are wearing one of my veils. I saw you trailing it in your food. Take it off, I don't want you wearing it.' Lunging at me she tries to rip it from my head. Stepping back I tell her I will go upstairs and change it. Before I get the chance, Mother Aloysius calls me to her office to tell me that the lay nun who should have been on her way to replace me is not coming and my work will continue in the refectory for another while.

★★★

I pray fervently that I will soon be relieved from the duties that are weighing so heavily upon me. Frightening dreams begin to invade my sleep … Menacing black shadows are inscribed on the wall above the altar in the chapel where the wooden crucifix hangs. A large beech tree crashes through the roof and the bloodied, tortured body of Jesus Christ falls from the crucifix onto the ground beside me. My screams break through the tomb-like silence, waking me … and the other sisters.

'Sh …sh,' they hiss all around. 'Go back to sleep!'

I sink, paralysed, beneath my blanket, trying to escape the vision filling my head but afraid to return to sleep.

Morning comes and I struggle through the day wishing for some relief from my tiredness. I have missed recreation and night prayers in the chapel and I haul myself upstairs to bed. Before I reach my cell, Sister Agatha beckons me along a dark, ghostly passageway that leads on to the open verandah at the back of the convent. 'Your bed is now out here because you are waking the other nuns during the night. This is where the lay nuns sleep when there is no cell for them. You will be allowed inside during storms and heavy rain.' She stares hard at my headdress. 'Why are you still wearing my veil when I told you I don't want you wearing it? It is heavily stained. You did the same with Sister Xavier's veils.' Her clenched fist comes down on the side of my head.

Pain pulses between my temples as I prepare for bed, making use of a thin strand of light shining from the heavens. An earthy smell hangs in the air and the sounds of rustling leaves and snapping branches echo around me as birds flit from tree to tree and small animals scrabble about the ground below. I burrow deep into bed with the blanket held tightly over my head to escape whirring wings and stinging insects. Alone and lost in this alien place, I wonder why God is not listening to my prayers.

Dawn creeps over Mount Erin and with unbearable closeness the thunderous vibration of the convent bell strikes like a hammer into my head. I crawl from under the blanket, tired and hungry, shivering in the chill of the morning air. I force myself along the passageway to dress and dutifully follow the line of nuns downstairs to chapel to begin the same routine as yesterday.

None of the junior nuns will swap beds with me and I ask Mother Aloysius, after breakfast, if I could have a separate cell.

'There are no separate cells for lay nuns.'

'I have been told there are two separate cells amongst the lay nuns, Mother.'

'So you have been mentioning it to the lay nuns?' Her frozen look tells me I will continue sleeping on the verandah.

I wake one morning shading my eyes from the bright light breaking through the darkness. A wave of nausea causes a merciless pounding in my head forcing me from my bed. I am unsure of the time as I dress and creep downstairs. Stepping outside, I walk about the dew-soaked gardens hoping for relief and meet Sister Veronica.

'It is not yet five o'clock, Sister,' she says.

'I am unwell with a headache. I think I will have to break my fast and eat something.'

'You will have to persevere and wait until after Mass.'

I lie on top of my bed trying to quell the sickness of hunger. The religious observance for receiving Holy Communion each morning at mass is to abstain from food and drink for twelve hours. Not even a sip of water can pass my lips. My headache remains with me all day and by bedtime I long for sleep. When I make my way upstairs, Sister Veronica is waiting for me.

'Your bed has been brought back inside, Sister. Don't disturb the other sisters during the night or you will have to sleep out on the verandah again.'

A small act of kindness, but as I prepare for bed I am plagued with doubts and am slowly losing faith. Almost two years have passed since I was placed in charge of the refectory and there is no end in sight.

Where did it all go wrong?

★★★

The elected office of Mother Superior rotates every three years and Mother Aloysius' term has come to an end. It passes again to Mother Stanislaus who I have already asked to be relieved of my duties in the refectory but she says there are no lay nuns to replace me. I despise the work and the continual complaints about the food.

Doctor William Joseph Dwyer was appointed the first Bishop of Wagga in 1918 and he visits Mount Erin once a year to speak to each sister individually. In May 1920, it is time for his annual visit and the tension builds as the sisters gather in a lengthy line outside Mother Stanislaus' office. I am queuing with the lay nuns quietly preparing what I will say. I will tell him that up until two years ago I was a choir nun, teaching in branch convents for six years, until I was relegated the duties of a lay nun. I will ask his advice on the proper measures that will allow me to return to teaching. Mother Stanislaus comes out of her office to tell us the Bishop is ready, and giving a harsh warning to be on our best behaviour. 'It is an honour that Bishop Dwyer is visiting Mount Erin. He will be asking each of you if you have any complaints to make and does not want to hear trifling protests of dissatisfaction.'

By the time my turn comes, my stomach is looped in knots. I knock and enter. Bishop Dwyer is tending the Reverend Mother's display of plants, his foot tapping time to the tune he is humming. He is wearing a scarlet red shoulder cape over his black cassock. A black silk band adorns his waist and a large cross set on a gold chain is draped around his neck, glistening amidst his dark clothing.

'I won't be a moment,' he says in a nonchalant manner, snapping dead leaves off a plant. Footsteps shuffle towards me, and I curtsey. He extends his right hand and I kiss his ring, a symbol of his faithfulness.

Ordered to sit down, I place my trembling hands into the big, roomy sleeves of my habit and fold them in my lap. He takes a seat behind the pine desk spreading his hands, the nails clipped short, across the polished surface. A few tufts of silver-grey hair poke from the sides of his smooth face. He is balding on top.

'I am asking all of the nuns in the convent these three questions.'

'Yes, Your Grace.'

'Are you in good health?'

'Yes, Your Grace.'

'You look very thin to me. Have you any complaints of any sort to make to me as bishop?'

'No, Your Grace.'

'Are you perfectly happy and contented?'

'Yes, Your Grace.'

Strict orders of obedience prevent me from answering otherwise.

Chapter Four

I look forward to playground duties with the children of St Mary's during break time. My teaching skills are useful settling squabbles and wiping tears after a fall. Spilling from their classrooms, a small group waits for me at the side gate near the chapel. Their button noses, sprinkled with freckles, poke through the metal railings as they listen for my key to jingle in the lock. The gate rattles open and they race forward, 'Sister Liguori ... please Sister Liguori ... let me hold your hand?'

Young Sheila Byrne, her face flushed with excitement, reaches me first and clasps my hand. Her little friends link hands on either side, forming a long daisy chain. We march in step across the playground, swinging our arms and chattering happily.

'My mother helped me pick a bunch of cream roses for you from our garden this morning, Sister.' Sheila's brown eyes glitter beneath her silken fringe: 'No one saw me bringing them into school and they're hidden in their usual spot behind the water tanks.'

I squeeze her hand. Sheila often brings me flowers. 'I must get you something special. I know, I will get you a holy card trimmed with paper lace,' I promise.

★★★

On Saturday, 24 July, I wake with a headache long before the calling bell and lie in the darkness wishing there was someone I could talk to. I have lost my place in this community as a choir nun and I no longer have Sister Raphael and Sister Kostka for company at recreation but the older lay nuns. How can I leave? Where will I go? How can I go into a world denied me so long? I recall the grief mixed with pride in Mama's eyes and the arguments with Dada when I took the first steps towards this life. It is sinful for me to have these thoughts and I shudder at where my mind is leading.

I wash in the pre-dawn chill and, yawning, raise my arms up to take the heavy layers of the habit over my head. I string the long rosary beads through a brown leather belt that buckles tighter around my thinning waist. I lace up my old boots, so tired and worn they can only be polished to a dull shine. Pinning my veil on to my headdress, I pick up my glasses and wrap their metal arms around my ears before emptying the water from my wash basin down the lavatory. I make my way to the chapel and, kneeling before the altar, the loud rumblings in my stomach remind me that several hours will pass before I will sit down to breakfast.

I have fewer duties at weekends and when I finish my work in the refectory, I go in search of the Mother Superior to ask if I could be allowed back to teaching. She usually brushes me off telling me it is the devil tempting me to turn my back on God. She was away for three weeks and only returned a few days ago. I visit the chapel where several solitary black figures are bent forward in prayer. Mother Stanislaus is not in her usual seat and I go to her office. There is no reply to my knock and I climb the stairs hoping to catch sight of her outside from one of the top windows. I press my face closer to the glass and am lost in the gathering gloom of ash-grey skies as I peer across the paddocks, sensing the freedom that lies beyond the convent grounds. In the strained light, two identical chimneys poke through a gap in the trees. Smoke patterns billow into the air and I wonder about the family living there. I glimpse the Mother Superior and rush back down to the office, trying to catch my breath before knocking the door.

'Excuse me, Mother, but I am so tired … I am finding it difficult to sleep and I have a headache.'

Without looking up, she says she will ask Doctor Leahy to prescribe something.

'I was also hoping to speak to you about returning to my former duties.'

She raises her head briefly. 'We have no lay nuns to replace you in the refectory. You are due in chapel now. Pray to God and offer your trials up to Him.'

I make my way to the chapel where I contemplate my calling to this life. Pray! It's all we ever do. Work and pray! Pray and work! How can I pray with this headache? It is almost midday. I genuflect and leave.

Returning to the refectory, I hear one of the sisters ask, 'When will dinner be ready?' I cast my eyes to the floor and ignore her. I wade through the swirling steam dragging two buckets brimming with potato and vegetable peelings towards the back door.

The rattle of cupboards draws my attention to a search going on. Sister Joan approaches, beckoning me for a word in the doorway. 'There is a broom missing from the community room. One of the sisters said you were using it.'

Several nuns gather to alert Sister Joan to a broom found in the cupboard under the stairs. Swinging around sharply, she accuses me of taking it. 'This broom is clearly marked Community Room! You were using it in the refectory.'

'I was not using it. Sister Gertrude must have put it there.'

The room freezes and every eye is upon me as she moves closer. Her spittle-flecked lips are inches from my face. 'Why are you blaming Sister Gertrude? YOU are a liar!' She turns on her heel and leaves, the other nuns trooping behind her.

Thoughts of despair veer through my head. *Is this how it feels when your spirit finally breaks?* Somehow I prompt myself back to duty. It is dinnertime and in a haze of self-doubt, I half-heartedly ladle vegetable soup into jugs and pass them to each table along with coarse loaves of bread. As soon as Grace is said and permission is given to eat, I fumble with my apron hastily folding it away to go in search of somewhere I can be alone. It's Saturday and there is no school. My legs are like tree stumps as I climb the back steps leading onto the deserted playground. Standing beneath a tree, rain drips from its branches and blends with the tears already rolling down my cheeks.

I want to berate God for calling me to this life. A life that has turned some of the sisters to gall and bitterness while their frail human natures become a prey to spite. Why is it a sin to give a loving thought to my beloved parents, to yearn for the closeness of my sisters and brother? Why is it a sin to form a friendship or an attachment for any person, place or thing? Why it is a sin to have a photograph, and why is it a sin even to admire a flower?

The roses! I remember the roses hidden behind the water tanks and make my way towards them, stopping for a moment at the nuns' cemetery to reflect on the deceased sisters. They lived in total seclusion, shut away from everything that is worth living for. They never left their enclosed convent, not even in death. Two of the first Irish nuns to arrive in Wagga are buried here, Sister Mary Evangelist Kelly and Mother Mary Xavier Byrne whose father, a Dublin architect, had drawn up the plans for Mount Erin Convent. When the building was complete, the Bishop walked the grounds and, finding a fallen branch, marked out a line of enclosure in the sand. Chains don't restrain me – just an illusory line.

What will happen if I go beyond this point on my own, without permission? One step is all it will take. I start walking across the fields. The soft rain rinses my tears away as my pace quickens and in a short time I have reached a road at the back of the convent. Wandering along the empty street, I stop at some railings and choose a house hidden behind thick bushes and trees.

I follow a path around the side of the house and knock, praying they will let me use their telephone. I am going to talk to the Bishop.

A young girl opens the door.

'Who is it, Marjory?' a female voice asks from inside.

'It's a nun, Mother.'

My stomach gurgles at the smells drifting from within, reminding me of my mother's busy kitchen at home stocked for the winter months. I haven't eaten since breakfast and the small bowl of thin porridge barely satisfied me. I lick my lips at thoughts of mouth-watering deep-filled pies crammed with sweet, juicy apples and the fruits of bumper crops. I think of Mama's freshly baked bread served warm from the oven with creamy butter and spread thickly with jam made from the plump, ripe blackberries picked from the hedgerows beside our home.

'Hello, can I help you?' a lady asks, eying my habit.

'My name is Sister Liguori. I am from the convent. Could I use the telephone?' I hold up my muddied hem and wipe my boots on a mat when she invites me inside. She introduces herself as Mrs Jessie Burgess and gets me the connection with the presbytery, leaving me alone to talk.

'I wish to speak to Bishop Dwyer.'

'Bishop Dwyer is away for a few days in Albury. This is Father Barry.'

'My name is Sister Liguori ... I am one of the nuns in the convent.'

'Are you phoning from the convent?'

'No, I am not. I am phoning from the home of Mrs Jessie Burgess in Wagga ... I had hoped to speak to Bishop Dwyer. Thank you. Goodbye,' Disappointed, I replace the receiver. *If only the Bishop had been at home.*

I pop my head around the kitchen door to Mrs Burgess. 'May I just stay here to rest for a while? There's been a little trouble at the convent and I would like to remain away until it blows over. I don't want to be any bother.'

'Yes, Sister, of course you can stay here. I'll take you into the dining room where you can warm yourself at the fire. Marjory will look after you while I make a pot of tea.'

The dining room is simply furnished with a table and four chairs. A set of pink-patterned cups and plates is displayed on a dresser that stands against the opposite wall alongside a wooden bookcase. The room is bright with the blaze of logs crackling and sparking in the grate. I sit down at the dining table and the little girl sits beside me.

'Marjory, show Sister Liguori the photograph album.'

Marjory lifts a large black family album down from the bookcase and places it on the dining table.

'Thank you, Marjory, and how old are you?'

'I'm twelve,' she says politely.

We look at the photographs together, turning each page slowly. Marjory points out cherished family scenes, those precious moments forever preserved. I look closely at the changing fashion of the ladies and their large-brimmed hats. I think of my sisters. Susan and Kathleen are married with children, but I have no photographs of them. I have no photographs of myself either, inside or outside of the convent. It is seen as self-glorification and is forbidden.

Mrs Burgess returns with a silver tray set with a large pot of tea, fine gold-rimmed china cups and a milk jug and sugar bowl bearing the same pattern. Pouring the tea, she offers me a slice of cake. It is such a treat to be served afternoon tea in someone's house.

Mrs Burgess moves to the window, remarking on the dreary day. 'There is a heavy mist in the air already and it looks like we're in for a foggy night, Sister. I hope you're warm enough.'

'Yes, thank you, Mrs Burgess,' I say, relaxing in the warmth of their home and their company. I hardly notice the hours passing and wonder whether things have settled at the convent. I jump to my feet when I hear the familiar sound of the convent bus. I lock the door and listen on the other side to the voice of the groom. My telephone call to the presbytery has alerted the convent to my whereabouts. 'I'm in trouble, Marjory ... I'm not supposed to leave the convent and I don't want to go back with him.'

'You can stay here with us for as long as you want,' the little girl says.

The groom returns to the convent, and another hour passes before the convent bus comes back with Mother Clare and Mother Aloysius.

Fearing the punishment for leaving the convent without permission, I refuse to unlock the door. After some persuasion from Mother Clare, I let her in. Marjory leaves us alone.

Mother Clare's cold, staring eyes are magnified behind her glasses. 'What were you thinking of? As soon as Father Barry got your phone call, he rang the convent. We searched everywhere for you, Sister. You do not look well. I think you are ill.'

'I wanted a rest. I am tired.'

'If you come back, the doctor will give you something to relieve you.'

'I don't need the doctor.'

'Reverend Mother is very anxious to see you,' Mother Clare insists.

I agree to return to a life I can no longer bear because I do not wish to be of any further trouble to Mrs Burgess. At the gate, I gently squeeze her arm, thanking her and whispering, 'Goodbye.'

Mother Aloysius and Mother Clare stare ahead as we journey back.

I have no hope for forgiveness. I have breached my vows. We pull up at the front door and I am ordered straight to the office. Mother Stanislaus is sitting behind her desk. Her head is bowed and she is reading some sort of official document. My stomach tightens when I see a copy of the Rules and Constitution of the Order lying open on her desk. I wait for her to look up. She rises slowly and walks towards me. Standing face to face she glares over the rim of her glasses, 'What have you got to say for yourself?'

'Mother, I am sorry.'

'Did someone in the convent do anything to make you go away?'

'No, Mother, you were all very kind to me.' She will not listen if I tell her otherwise.

'Go and change those wet clothes. I have arranged for Doctor Leahy to examine you.' She dismisses me into the charge of Sister Brendan. 'Take her to get something to eat while we wait for the doctor.'

A boiled egg and some toast along with a cup of tea is set in front of me in the kitchen. I eat slowly pondering the incident. 'Did you hear the noise in here earlier?' I ask Sister Brendan.

'What noise?'

'There was a disturbance about a broom!'

'I know nothing of any disturbance … only the one *you* caused!'

★★★

As soon as the doctor arrives, I am sent for. Entering the office, I overhear Mother Stanislaus saying, 'I regard her leaving the convent as a very serious breach. I don't think she realizes she has broken Canon Law. What must those people in Wagga think of her? More to the point, what will her mother think of her?'

The mention of Canon Law reminds me of the threat of excommunication, but Mother Stanislaus knows that mentioning my mother will cause me greater pain. I meant no harm but I will never be allowed to forget my brief lapse. The incident is not over. I will be reminded of this every day for the rest of my life.

The convent doctor, William Leahy, is an Irishman who came to Australia in the mid-1890s. He is of medium build and is wearing a black suit with a white shirt and dark tie. His shiny bald patch is offset by grey hair smoothed neatly down each side of his head. He places his medical bag on to a table to begin a brief examination and I feel the Reverend Mother's fixed stare burning through my back while he checks my pulse and notes that my heart is going very quickly.

'You are run down, Sister. Were you not taking the medicine I prescribed for you before?' His manner is distinctly impatient.

'I needed a tonic and the medicine you prescribed had to be taken at bedtime and then I was unable to sleep.' He asks no further questions and turns his back to me to talk to Mother Stanislaus. 'I will issue a prescription. In the meantime, it is rest.' The Angelus bell chimes and we kneel down to recite prayers. I am then ordered to bed. Sister Brendan, who currently is in charge of the dispensary, is instructed to remain with me to administer the prescribed medicine as soon as the local chemist makes it up.

Sister Brendan takes me upstairs and I put on my nightgown while she fetches water for me to have a wash.

'My headdress is wet – I will need a fresh one for the morning.'

'Here's one … it is Sister Agatha's.'

'Oh please, no, I beg you, not Sister Agatha's! Her veils are too long and when I wore one of hers before, she thumped me for letting it trail in my food.'

'It's the only one that is likely to fit.'

I pull the white cap over my head and tuck the strings in underneath before setting the long veil beside my habit that is neatly folded for Mass in the morning. While I wash, Sister Brendan offers to make up my bed.

'I am well able to make it myself.'

She sprinkles holy water around the cell and tells me to get into bed before sprinkling more holy water over me. Sister Brendan goes downstairs to collect the medicine leaving me alone to puzzle over her actions. We usually sprinkle our own holy water. Only on one occasion have I seen this done before – when a sister was dying and unable to sprinkle her own.

She returns with an array of bottles and phials and standing with her back to me, she measures out a dose. 'Here, take this.'

I look suspiciously at the contents of the cup. 'Why am I being given medicine? I am not sick.'

'It is castor oil prepared in a cup of coffee. It is what the doctor prescribed. I've also brought you a biscuit.' She holds the cup to my mouth, telling me to drink it. A thick fur coats my tongue and I push it away, spluttering. 'What is this foul stuff? It tastes like ink!'

Sister Brendan forces me to finish it. 'Lie still and have a good sleep so that the oil does not repeat!' She removes my pillow and lays my arms crosswise on my breast.

'You won't want another dose because you won't be getting out of that bed for the next six months!' She places two candles on either side of me, lighting them before retiring to another part of the room.

The candles burn dimly, their ghostly flickering sparking more fear into me. What *did* the doctor prescribe? It tasted like poison. Was it poison or was it a sleeping draught? Whatever it was, I must rid myself of it before it goes through my whole system. Fighting to stay awake, I ask for a cup of cocoa.

'It is rather soon after the medicine. I will get you a cup later.'

At 7.30 p.m., Mother Stanislaus sends for Sister Brendan but before she goes downstairs her ever-watchful eyes peer around the curtain. I pretend I am sleeping.

As soon as her footsteps fade, I force myself out of bed and gulp down three cups of soapy water from my basin. I keep my hands over my mouth to hold back the sickly surge of rising bile and dash to the lavatory. I lock the door quickly behind me and am just in time to spill the dark contents of my stomach down the bowl, before slumping onto the hard floor.

The door handle rattles. 'Open this door, Sister! Why are you out of bed? You will die of pneumonia. It is a wonder you are not dead now.'

'My feet are so cold,' I call out weakly, 'would you go downstairs for a hot water bottle? I will be in bed when you return.'

Listening for a moment, from the other side of the door, I turn the key slowly. Within seconds I am racing down the back stairs and along a dimly lit corridor, my feet skimming its polished surface. I try one of the window latches. It will not budge and I move to the next one, yanking it hard. I push my way through the narrow opening and crawl out on to the ledge. My feet scrape against the rough surface as I brace myself for the painful drop to the ground. I land barefoot in a pool of swirling mist and take a moment to recover. A single shaft of light guides me along the path I had taken earlier. The rough ground tears at the soles of my feet as I dash headlong into thick, grey fog. My toes stump hard against sharp rocks and, losing my footing, I am tossed forward, rolling dangerously close to the edge of a waterhole. I lie breathless with the freezing chill probing my bones. I have lost my glasses and can see nothing. Groping about the dirt beside me, I find them and put them on, straining to see behind. The convent and its lights have vanished.

Please, God … help me! I can't go back!

I rip off my headdress, throwing it to the ground. 'Sister Agatha, you will NEVER thump me again!'

A dog's bark in the distance unmuzzles the eerie silence. Years of overcoming weakness now provides me with the strength to get onto my feet and keep going. At last, the house appears. Staggering towards it, I rap the door and take cover behind some shrubs. The door opens and Mrs Burgess peers out, her bewildered face unsure of the ghostly figure emerging shoeless from the shadows.

'Here I am, frightening you again.'

'Sister Liguori!' She exclaims, half smothering her cry.

Shivering in a white nightgown clinging to my skin, I try to shield my exposed head with my hands. She reaches out to help me inside. 'Please don't let anyone take me back to the convent.'

'I will help you, Sister. Please don't worry. You can stay here for the night.'

'But this will be the first house they will search!' I am too afraid to stay and beg her to take me further away.

'I will keep you safe, Sister. Let me quickly bathe your feet, they are cut and bruised.' The warm soapy water soothes my burning soles and Mrs Burgess gently removes grit and dirt wedged between my toes.

'I was thinking about you all evening, wondering how you fared when you went back to the convent.'

'I didn't fare too well. I am now done with convent life for good, but I have nothing and I know no one in Australia.'

She assures me of her help and gives me a pair of shoes and a coat, then she wraps a thick buggy blanket around me to cover my head. Its warmth spreads instant heat through my body. Holding on to each other, we half-walk, half-run through the dark, deserted streets in the shadowy glow of the street lamps, checking behind at regular intervals to see if anyone is following. When we arrive at the Church of England Hostel, it is closed for the night. Not disheartened, Mrs Burgess suggests the Thompsons who live behind the convent in Coleman Street.

Chapter Five

MOUNT ERIN CONVENT

'Sister Liguori has vanished!' A high-pitched shriek shatters the silence.

Mother Stanislaus watches horrified as Sister Brendan comes clattering down the stairs, her habit trailing behind her. The Mother Superior hastily leads her into her office.

'I have searched everywhere she might be. She is nowhere to be found, Mother. I stayed with her as you directed. I settled her into bed, making sure she was comfortable. We prayed together and I promised I would get her a cup of cocoa to help her sleep. When she complained that her feet were cold, I offered to go downstairs and get her a hot water bottle. I was only away for a short time but when I returned she was gone.' Her voice drops to a whisper. 'Mother, her habit is folded in her cell and her boots are still under her bed.'

'It is another act of defiant disobedience,' the Reverend Mother snaps, already holding the telephone in her hand. 'I will call the presbytery and some of the local people.'

Several nuns on their way to recreation hear the commotion and crowd into the room. 'Go and search the convent for Sister Liguori,' Mother Stanislaus orders. 'Sister Brendan, wait here with me while I telephone Father Barry.'

The priest says he will telephone the police and instructs the Reverend Mother to get hold of Doctor Leahy. She also rings several neighbours.

Sergeant O'Rourke takes the call in Wagga and dispatches two police officers. They arrive within fifteen minutes. Constable Brownlow, the older officer, asks for a brief description of the missing nun while Constable O'Rourke scribbles down notes. 'How long has she been missing?'

'The alarm was raised about twenty minutes ago. She doesn't seem to be anywhere in the convent but some of the sisters are still searching,' Mother Stanislaus informs him.

Constable Brownlow checks his watch. 'It's now shortly after eight p.m. It's important we start searching as quickly as possible. Have you any idea where she would go?'

'We observe strict rules of enclosure and no one is allowed to leave the convent without my permission. Earlier today, Sister Liguori left the grounds and went to the home of Mr and Mrs Frank and Jessie Burgess at the back of the convent where she remained for several hours. I sent two sisters down in the convent bus to bring her back. The doctor examined her on her return and she was sent to bed. I put Sister Brendan in charge of her. She went downstairs to get a hot water bottle for her and when she returned, the sister was gone. We believe she is barefoot, dressed only in her nightgown.'

The police officers gather a search party together while the nuns continue scouring the inside of the convent, praying for the safe return of their sister. The widening search into the neighbouring paddocks and along the railway line becomes more difficult with dense fog draped everywhere. Two hours later, Constable O'Rourke returns to the convent along with some local men who have joined the search for the missing sister.

'This headdress was lying in the mud at the edge of a waterhole,' the constable says.

An uneasy silence chokes the room when Sister Brendan stammers, 'Earlier this evening, Sister Liguori asked me for a fresh headdress because hers was wet. I gave her that one … it was Sister Agatha's.' Her bony fingers fidget with the long string of rosary beads hanging from the black leather belt of her habit.

The Reverend Mother gazes out of the window at the wall of

thick grey fog encircling the convent. Her unforgiving voice says to all those present, '*Who would go out on a night like this in her bare feet, wearing only a nightgown? She must be mad!*'

Chapter Six

T he dogs are working themselves into a frenzy at the crowd gathering at our front gate, Robert,' Mrs Thompson tells her husband.

There is a heavy knock on the front door and crouching in the shadows of a stranger's kitchen, I listen to the conversation between Mr Thompson and a police constable. They have found my headdress and are searching the houses in the neighbourhood where it is rumoured I have taken refuge.

'I am sure you will understand the sisters are concerned on such a dreadful night. They have conducted their own search within the convent but they cannot search beyond and have asked the police to help. We have combed the convent grounds and several townspeople are also helping.'

'They say she's running around in her nightdress and that she is mad!' a man's voice shouts in the distance.

'Will you ring the station if you see or hear anything?'

'Wait, Constable, there is something …'

The beat of my heart grows louder, drumming hard into my chest and I hold my breath to stop any sound escaping. Please God, no! … Don't let them send me back to the convent.

'… Please move these people away from our property. It is upsetting my wife.' Mr Thompson closes the door abruptly behind him.

Breathing freely again, I wonder, how did I doubt these people? I am safe among friends.

'I ran the risk that a Good Samaritan would take me in,' I tell Mrs Thompson when she hands me a cup of cocoa.

'Cradle its warmth in your freezing fingers,' she says. I savour the sweet liquid trickling down my throat after the sourness of the medicine. Suddenly I realize the enormity of what I have done and my hands start shaking, spilling my cocoa. I cannot hold back as I unleash my troubles on a total stranger. Mrs Thompson listens sympathetically as I relate the day's events, finally telling her about Sister Brendan's suspicious acts, forcing me to flee the convent, fearing for my life.

'We are Protestants and you will be safe with us,' Mrs Thompson says, reassuringly. 'As you know, a Catholic family would send you back to the convent. You need something to wear. You are about the same size and height as my sister. She will lend you some of her clothes.'

'Thank you, Mrs Burgess was right when she left me in your care, saying I would be among friends. Did you know I could see the tall chimneys of this house from inside the convent? I often looked out from the upstairs window wondering who lived here.'

'It was to be two-storey, which is why the ceilings are so high. The house was built for the Mayor of Wagga, George Coleman. The street is named after him. Now, what are we going to call you?'

'My name is Brigid Partridge.'

Miss Ethel Heathwood arrives a short time later with some clothing. Mrs Thompson introduces me to her sister who shows me several dresses and suggests a green floral print that will remind me of Ireland. There is also a matching scarf that I can throw over my head.

Peeping through a small gap in the curtains, Miss Heathwood notices a man has climbed one of the trees outside for a better view. 'Come and have a look. The cheek of him! He is actually taking photographs!'

'He looks a little shaky. I wonder, is he going to fall off,' Mrs Thompson quips.

Mr Thompson is concerned at the increasing numbers of Catholic pickets outside his home. 'It seems that Wagga has split into two over this – Catholic and Protestant,' he says, before stepping onto the verandah, threatening, 'Get off my property or I will release my dogs on you.'

I am offered a bedroom at the side of the house where I will not be seen and where I can rest, but nobody gets peace to sleep as noises from the search party filter through the house all night along with flashing torches lighting up the darkness.

By Sunday morning, the fog is slowly lifting, leaving patches of mist hanging over Wagga. To avoid the local telephone exchange overhearing their conversation, Mrs Thompson instructs her sister to go to the nearby Church of England hostel to make two telephone calls. First, Miss Heathwood rings the police station to arrange for the police inspector to go to the Church of England hostel. Secondly, she is to ring Doctor Eric Tivey, who practises at Wagga, and ask him also to go to the hostel. When they arrive there, the Matron passes on the message that they are both wanted at a nearby residence in Coleman Street.

'Who is it? Have they come to take me back?' I call out from the bedroom when I hear the sound of men's voices in the hall.

Mrs Thompson accompanies a gentleman into the bedroom. 'I have asked the local doctor to examine you in view of the crowd outside branding you "mad".'

'My name is Doctor Tivey.' His voice is gentle, reassuring. He suggests I sit by the window where the light is better and waits for me to sit down before pulling up a chair to face me. His dark suit fits snugly across his square shoulders and his black hair is brushed into a quiff above his forehead with the sides creased down smoothly.

'Why did you leave the convent?'

'I have been rather run down lately. The work I had been called upon to do had been heavier than my health would stand.'

'What was the work?'

'I had been placed on duty in the refectory. I was promised that I would be relieved in a fortnight by a lay nun. I remained there for two years. I had to do scrubbing and sweeping and washing dishes and waiting on table. I was also called upon to take trays to any of the sisters who may be ill. I was expected to carry out in five or ten minutes, tasks that would ordinarily take me half an hour. In addition, I had to attend prayers and various religious observances.'

The doctor's manner is friendly compared to Doctor Leahy, who showed little interest in my medical complaints and often appeared in a rush.

'Do you have any illness?'

'I have only been run down and the convent doctor attended to me in the past.'

After a brief physical examination, Doctor Tivey states he cannot detect any sign of illness. 'Would you go back to the convent?'

'No,' I answer, a little too quickly.

We go into the parlour where Inspector Duprez and Constable Cooper are waiting. The doctor confirms his opinion that I am perfectly sane. Inspector William Duprez introduces himself, saying he wishes to ask me a few questions. He is a heavyset man with greying hair who tells me he is looking forward to his retirement after thirty-three years with the police.

'Are you the nun who left the convent yesterday?'

'Yes.'

'How long had you been in there?'

'Over ten years.'

'By Jove, you look very young ... what age are you?'

'I am twenty-eight.'

'Do you want to go back?'

'No ... not if I can help it.'

'I don't know of any law to compel you to go back if you don't want to,' the inspector assures me.

'Mrs Thompson is going to look after me for the present.'

'Is that correct?'

'Yes, that's correct, Inspector.'

★★★

Happier to have spoken to both the doctor and the inspector, I ask Mrs Thompson for a pen, some writing paper and an envelope. I must write to the Bishop to be freed from my vows. Dipping the fine gold nib into the black ink brings a rising sensation to my throat and mouth, a reminder of last night's vile medicine. I can smell the awful stuff everywhere. It prompts me to give deep thought to what I wish to say to the Bishop. Writing in my best handwriting, I check over my letter several times before folding it into an envelope.

Word that the doctor and police inspector both visited the Thompson household confirms reports that I am inside and the gathering crowd swells in numbers. Mr Thompson makes several phone calls seeking advice.

Father Barry delivers a letter from the Reverend Mother along with a parcel of clothing but Mrs Thompson refuses to take the parcel, saying they will provide for all my needs. She gives Father Barry my letter for the Bishop.

★★★

That evening, I am told arrangements are in place to get me away from Wagga, and, preparing to leave, I change into a long, powder blue dress. The weightless cotton falls around me, lightly brushing against my skin. A pair of sheer nylon stockings is placed delicately on the bed. Ultra-fine, they bear no semblance to the thick woollen ones I am used to. From a selection of shoes, I pick a black pair with a small heel before stealing a timid glance at my reflection in the mirror. I am shocked at my thinning outline and the coarse hair poking like wild bracken from my pink scalp.

'I have the perfect solution,' Mrs Thompson says, reading my thoughts. She pulls a grey knitted cap down over my head and offers me a warm brown sports coat to wear. 'When you turned up on our doorstep last night, you were filled with the fear of a hunted animal. Now, look at you: the outfit puts colour on your cheeks and matches those beautiful blue eyes. I don't think anyone will recognize you.'

Several friends have called at the house for afternoon tea and the steady flow of conversation in the room stops when I appear.

'Are we ready?' Mrs Thompson asks as some of her friends walk out of the front door. 'You're next, Brigid, but I'll be right behind you,' Mrs Thompson says.

'I hope I don't trip in these heels.'

A gentleman gallantly offers me his arm. Tucking mine into his,

I take a few deep breaths before walking leisurely down the path, casually chatting away as we stroll past the unsuspecting pickets. Tempted to look back to see if Mrs Thompson is following, we cross the road to get clear of the house and gather into a small group under some trees to await the arrival of a car. Unnoticed, we watch the pickets from that spot for twenty minutes, amused as they change guard.

'We are taking you to another sister of mine who lives forty miles away in Adelong,' Mrs Thompson says, slipping into the back seat beside me along with the gentleman who had guided me through the pickets. Another gentleman jumps into the front seat beside the driver.

'You can be sure of one thing, Mrs Thompson, I will never forget your kindness.'

I watch the road ahead, looking out at the flat plains of New South Wales. Darkness descends quickly. My eyelids are heavy from lack of sleep. The general conversation with my new companions slowly dies away and the rhythmic hum of the motor overpowers me as I drift into oblivion.

We arrive at Mount Pleasant at 11.30 that night.

'This is my sister, Mrs Letitia Howell, and this is Miss Brigid Partridge,' says Mrs Thompson.

After supper, Mrs Thompson and the other gentlemen are ready to return to Wagga. Before leaving I hear her telling her sister, 'I love the little girl and I think I should have first claim on her, but so long as she gets her freedom, we will all be happy. Still, I must see her again.'

'You may be feeling a little anxious now that my sister has left,' Mrs Howell says, 'but you are free to do as you please while you are here with me, Brigid.'

'Will you give me protection if anyone comes for me? Please don't give me up!'

'I promise I will take care of you.'

Deep red curtains dress the small windows in the bedroom. The bed is made up with delicate linen sheets folded down over a thick embroidered blanket.

Mrs Howell notices me yawning. 'I will leave you alone now. It is very late. There is a nightdress under the pillow. Good night, and I hope you sleep well.'

'I'm frightened of being on my own.'

'Would you like me to stay a while?'

'You are so very kind, Mrs Howell. Thank you.'

I wake several times during the night in the strangeness of my new surroundings. Finally, when morning arrives, there is no thunderous convent bell and no headache, just the gentle stirrings of a family home. I lie for a while thinking about the convent. It is Monday and the children will be waiting for me at the gate beside the chapel. I wonder what they will think when they hear that *Sister Liguori ran away on a foggy winter's night?*

Chapter Seven

THE PRESBYTERY, WAGGA WAGGA

Bishop Dwyer returns from Albury on Monday evening. Striding into the parlour, he demands to know, 'Where is Sister Liguori now?'

'We believe she is still with the Thompsons in Coleman Street,' Father Barry informs him.

'Those heretics! How jubilant will they be having "an escaped nun" in their grip!'

Father Barry is more than aware of the Bishop's feelings. Being the Australian-born son of Irish migrants, the Bishop takes a keen interest in Irish-Australian politics. He is not afraid to express anti-British and pro-Irish sentiments, heightened by the ongoing struggle of the Irish people against the British Crown.

'The Thompsons asked me to give this to you. It is from Sister Liguori.'

The Bishop reads the letter and dismisses it into the corner of his pine writing desk, telling Father Barry, 'I will deal with the matter in the morning,' before retiring to bed.

The Bishop wakes early and after a hearty breakfast, he calls at the convent to hear a first-hand account of the incident from Mother Stanislaus. He listens to her thoughts on the inappropriate way Sister Liguori had left the convent making her conclude that the sister was mad. She informs him that Doctor Tivey had attended Sister Liguori on Sunday and as far as he knew, she was quite normal, was not in bed, and had not contracted cold. The Bishop is also informed that Inspector Duprez had interviewed Sister Liguori. Returning to the Presbytery, the Bishop writes a letter to the Thompsons and then replies to Sister Liguori, enclosing a copy of his letter to the Thompsons.

He then calls at the office of Inspector Duprez in Wagga telling him he needs to deliver his letters and speak with the sister. The inspector offers to drive him to the Thompson residence and on the way they discuss Sister Liguori's irrational behavior. The inspector says that when he interviewed her on Sunday she appeared to be perfectly sane.

Arriving at the house, Mrs Thompson informs him that Sister Liguori left on Sunday afternoon.

'I don't believe it! She was seen here this morning,' the Bishop argues.

'You can believe it or not – she has not been here since Sunday. You can come in and search if you wish.' The Bishop declines the offer, giving the Thompsons their letter, but withholding his letter to Sister Liguori.

★★★

By Thursday, 29 July, the police have lost all trace of Sister Liguori and the Bishop considers the only course of action left open to him is to procure a warrant for her detention. He telephones Doctor Leahy and asks him if he expresses the opinion that the sister is deranged in her mind. The doctor agrees that she is and offers to write a certificate to that effect. Mr James Sheekey, a solicitor who practices in Wagga, and a faithful member of the Catholic community, is assigned to draw up an affidavit. He meets with the Bishop on 31 July to show him a copy and informs him he had attended the chamber magistrate's office in Wagga, along with Doctor Leahy, to ask for a warrant for Sister Liguori's arrest. Mr Hazell *(chamber magistrate)* had refused, saying he was not convinced that she was insane because Doctor Tivey had said she was perfectly sane. He would want to visit the patient and see for himself what she was like.

At pains as to how to recover Sister Liguori, Mr Sheekey advises the Bishop to take the matter to Sydney. The Bishop returns to the Presbytery to retrieve the letter from the corner of his writing desk, resolving 'by hook or by crook' he will get Sister Liguori out of the hands of those extremists!

Chapter Eight

I spend four wonderful days relaxing in the company of my new friends in Adelong, a pleasant, sleepy, rural settlement on the banks of the Adelong River. We go for walks every day. On Thursday, Mrs Howell's face is grey with worry: 'My brother-in-law, Robert Thompson, telephoned saying religious tension is heightening in Wagga and my two sisters are suffering for their role in your escape. They are being verbally abused in the street.'

'I have caused you good people too much trouble already. Today, I will write to my brother, Joseph. He moved to China last year to work in a business house in Hong Kong. He will give me advice and help me get home to Ireland.'

Mrs Howell offers to register the letter to ensure that he gets it.

In view of what's happening in Wagga, I become increasingly anxious and suspicious of everybody who passes by. Mrs Howell is worried and takes me to the local hospital. They advise rest.

I tell Mrs Howell that I am fearful I am still too close to Wagga and will be found and taken back to the convent. She seeks advice from her sister.

A gentleman arrives after midnight on Friday. In his fifties, his greying hair is combed into a side parting and smoothed flat on his head. He introduces himself as Mr Robert Elvin Barton and updates us on the situation in Wagga.

'I hear the Roman Catholic community there is making every effort to recover you; they are watching the railways and highways to ensure you don't escape. Your friends have asked me to take care of you and find you a place where you can be properly looked after and provided for.'

He speaks with such authority that I agree to travel with him and his daughter to Sydney.

The roads are heavy with water and mud and a short distance outside Adelong the car comes to a grinding halt. We scramble out on to the roadside and wait several hours for another vehicle before continuing the seventy-mile journey through the night.

At Cootamundra, we board the seven o'clock train to Sydney the following morning. As the train lurches forwards, I look out at the countryside, undisturbed. We pass through small hamlets of houses on either side of the railway tracks with only their roofs visible from the train. We stop at several stations and, when I catch sight of a priest boarding, I become alarmed. He chooses our compartment, placing his bag on the floor beside me. I shift uncomfortably in my seat and turn towards the window to avoid any conversation with him.

At noon on Saturday, 31 July, we arrive at 1 Chapel Street, Kogarah, which is on the outskirts of Sydney. Mr Barton introduces me to my new guardians.

The congregational minister, the Reverend William Touchell, reaches his hand out in greeting. He is in his fifties, white-haired and ruddy-faced. His wife, Laura, who appears to be around the same age, smiles warmly, saying, 'You have come to us by reason of another lady I know who had once been in a convent. When this young woman heard of your plight, she said, "Send her to the Touchells," and so you have come.' Mrs Touchell embraces me and welcomes me into their home.

She has prepared a light lunch and we sit down to slices of cold meat, fresh bread and butter and a cup of hot, sweet tea.

When Mr Barton and his daughter are leaving, I offer my thanks for getting me safely away from Wagga. Mrs Touchell tells me I will see them again soon. She shows me into a bedroom that has been prepared for my visit. It is a small room that holds a bed, a cupboard and a dressing table. She has left towels and linens for my use. She asks if I would like to lie down.

'I think I am too excited to sleep now.'

'Those borrowed clothes will have to be returned and I suggest a trip into town to do some shopping.'

I am setting my foot back into a world I do not know. The streets are filled with Saturday shoppers snaking their way through the crowded shops. I shy away at the sound of a motor horn and Mrs Touchell grips my hand. She promises we will not be too long. She is concerned about my short, unkempt hair and guides me into a milliner's shop. I want to pull away, but realize how ungrateful that would be. I trust this lady who has so willingly offered me a home for as long as I need it. The shop assistants help me choose a white hat with a wide rim, decorated with a lacy ribbon. In other shops, the young lady assistants, hoping to make a sale, offer their advice in selecting a new wardrobe for me. I am filled with excitement at the end of our shopping trip. Mrs Touchell has bought me a dress, a fitted blouse, a pleated skirt, a coat and a pair of comfortable shoes.

Several visitors arrive in the evening.

'To allay suspicion, I will tell a pardonable fib,' whispers Mrs Touchell. 'Miss Jones here is one of those girls who considers it beneficial to the hair to have it cut short.' Later, she confides, 'If any of them suspected that "Miss Jones" was ex-Sister Liguori, they were sports enough not to reveal it.'

At first, Mr Touchell appears stern but, within moments, he has reached out, generously offering his home and his protection.

'Is there anything you would like to do?' Mrs Touchell asks one afternoon as we sit on the verandah.

'I would just like to sit out here in the sun with you.'

'You are with us only a short time and I already feel you are the daughter I never had. I could listen to your sweet Irish accent all day ... so tell me about the convent. Twelve years is a long time.'

'I entered the convent, shutting myself away from the outside world, believing it to be the proper life to lead. I wanted to offer my life to God. I prayed that He would give me the strength I needed to serve Him. With time, I realized that, although it might be suitable for many women, I was temperamentally unfit for it.'

Mrs Touchell helps me through the ordeal of the past two weeks.

Slowly, I adjust to life outside the convent and as I regain my strength, my head becomes clearer and I look forward to outings and trips in the big open car.

It is eleven days since I fled the convent and Mr Barton, on one of his visits, reports that the incident is breaking in the local newspapers in Wagga. He has heard unofficially that Bishop Dwyer has sworn an information against me saying that I am of unsound mind.

Mr Touchell, seeing how upset I am, tries to reassure me. 'Anybody who says you are insane is insane himself. You have been with us for almost two weeks. You are a sweet, inoffensive, sane girl. The Bishop is enraged that you have turned to Protestants for help and he is trying to prevent a scandal for himself by saying you are "of unsound mind".'

'We will prove you are not insane,' Mrs Touchell says indignantly. 'I will contact the local doctor. He will assess you and provide us with a medical opinion as to your sanity.'

Doctor Binns arrives at seven p.m.

'Tell me about your medical history,' he says, his accent suggesting he's Scottish.

'I have had minor illnesses, but nothing serious.'

He checks my heart and lungs and temperature, all of which are entirely normal.

'Is there any mental or neurotic trouble in your family?'

'No.'

'Are your parents alive?'

'Both my parents are alive and well.'

Dr Binns asks me if I can remember comparatively recent events and his mild manner assures me I have answered to his satisfaction. He listens sympathetically to my reason for leaving the convent.

'I was a teaching sister, but was taken off teaching duties to do the domestic work in the convent. My determination to leave was arrived at suddenly, but I had been tired of the life for a couple of months before. My future movements are dependent upon my brother. He will be coming from China.'

'Well, there's nothing in your answers to suggest insanity,' he concludes, turning to Mrs Touchell. 'She strikes me as a rather unsophisticated, mentally normal person. She is a little restrained and a little reserved.'

★★★

B y Friday, my name screams from the headlines of newspapers throughout Australia and New Zealand.

Chapter Nine

'Your unfortunate situation is stirring up a blaze of publicity,' Mr Touchell says, handing me some newspapers.

A MISSING NUN
LEFT THE CONVENT IN HER NIGHTDRESS

Wagga, Wednesday — Much excitement has been created here owing to the disappearance of a nun, Sister Liguori, from the Mount Erin Convent. Miss Brigid Partridge (28) is a native of Ireland and came to Australia eleven years ago and entered the convent, taking up the name of Sister Liguori. On Saturday night, July 24, she left the convent in a nightdress, was sheltered at a neighbouring house for the night and has since disappeared. Inspector Duprez today said the police in Wagga have no knowledge whatever of her present whereabouts.

Sydney, Thursday — Following upon the sworn information of the Right Reverend Bishop Dwyer of Wagga, Mr Camphin, Chamber Magistrate, at the Central Police Court today issued a warrant for the arrest of Brigid Partridge, otherwise known as Sister Mary Liguori, of the Wagga Convent. The information of Dr Dwyer was that Sister Liguori, who recently left the convent, was of unsound mind.

The warrant has been handed to the police for execution. It directs the attendance of the accused at the Sydney Lunacy Court.

— Queanbeyan Age and Queanbeyan Observer,
Friday, 6 August, 1920

A feeling of nausea creeps over me as I read the cruel charges laid against me. 'Why is the Bishop making such allegations? I have sent in my resignation. I will present myself to the Bar of Justice on Monday morning in order to clear my name. In the meantime I will try to put the worry of it out of my head.'

'We know your faith in God will continue even if you have lost faith in man,' Mrs Touchell says.

The following evening, Saturday, two police officers arrive on the front doorstep. They introduce themselves as Detective Farley and Sergeant Harrowsmith and say they want to search the house, but Mr Touchell refuses them entry without the possession of a warrant. It is at police headquarters and the two officers return to Sydney. Without wishing to cause alarm, Mrs Touchell gently suggests we pack a few things. 'There may be the possibility of a motor run if they come back later.'

I change into one of my new outfits, a black skirt, and a blue striped blouse with a matching blue ribbon tie.

Just before midnight, heavy footsteps approach the house, followed by a strong knock. Mr Touchell opens the door to the two police officers who had called earlier and five uniformed policemen.

'This is the lady in question. Have a talk to her yourself and see if you think she is insane,' Mr Touchell offers.

The police officers gather into the room, and Detective Farley shows me the warrant. I barely hear his words. 'I am arresting you on the authority of the order given me … a person deemed to be insane and without sufficient means of support … to bring you before a magistrate to be dealt with according to the law.'

I slump to the floor and Mrs Touchell is at my side, cradling me in her arms. 'You are not guilty of breaking any law in this country. Only lawbreakers are punished. You have done nothing wrong.'

Hard, rough tears come and I am helped into a chair.

'I have sent in my resignation to the Bishop. Why is he making all this fuss?'

'I cannot say,' Detective Farley says.

'It is my intention to surrender myself to the authorities at nine a.m. on Monday morning.'

'I want you to come with me now to Sydney.'

Mrs Touchell demands to know where they are taking me. 'The Reception House for the Insane at Darlinghurst.' My hand flies to my tightening chest. I beg them to let Mrs Touchell accompany me. Detective Farley agrees.

Mrs Touchell advises me to wear my warm gaberdine coat and I am escorted from the house to the waiting police car, flanked by police officers. The commotion attracts the attention of the neighbours, who shout their support as the car drives off. During the journey, I confide to the young officer sitting beside me, 'Now that I know what I have to face I shall be glad to go on with it in order to have it settled. I shall never go back. I am sick and tired of it. It is like prison. I would rather remain in the hands of the police than go back to the convent.'

It is late when we arrive at the reception house in Darlinghurst and I am led into the sandstone building and taken to Admissions where paperwork is filled out. Ordered to hand over any valuables to the nurse on duty, I empty the contents of my pockets – a small roll of coins wrapped in brown paper. It is counted and amounts to £1.19s.6d. My money, given to me by well-wishers, is confiscated.

'Mrs Touchell can remain with you until you are brought before the Lunacy Court on Monday.' The matron's words comfort us. At least we can be under the same roof. The police, too, are relieved from driving Mrs Touchell the seven miles back to Kogarah.

In the early hours of Sunday morning, the heavy metal door slams shut behind us and we are locked into a small cell with two beds and a table, similar to the cramped space I occupied in the convent.

I look around at the grimy walls and the scuffed, worn floors. The cracked enamel sink where we have to wash is stained brown. The lights flash a warning that they will soon be turned off. 'I have no fears for the future and I am perfectly confident that my sanity is unquestionable,' I tell Mrs Touchell before saying goodnight and lowering myself into a bed wreathed in a malodorous mixture of foul decay.

Later that day, after little sleep, I am informed I have visitors and listen politely as they introduce themselves.

'My name is Patrick Joseph Minahan and this is my wife. I am a politician and a Member of the Legislative Assembly. For thirteen years I've interested myself on behalf of many persons of all creeds who are in need of a friend. I therefore asked my dear wife, Mrs Minahan, to accompany me here for the purpose of finding out the facts of your case. While many anti-Catholics could interview you at Wagga, no Catholic was permitted to see you and speak to you.'

'That was the newspapers saying that. I am not going back to the convent. I will lead a good Catholic life in the world and seek employment.'

Mr Minahan offers me a situation as companion to his wife.

'I am not in a position to accept your offer. I have to await the outcome of this charge against me.' I mistrust their intentions and am happy when they leave. I return to my room and my mood lifts when I am told I will be allowed reading books and my needlework and knitting.

The Lunacy Court sits alongside the reception house and often attracts a gawping crowd. On Monday, 9 August 1920, it is no different. I am told a big crowd of both Catholics and Protestants have gathered, both attempting a show of strength, shouting slogans and cheering and booing. With less than twenty seats, accommodation into the court is strictly limited. A uniformed nurse leads me to my seat and Mrs Touchell follows.

Mr Barton has arranged for Mr Francis Stewart Boyce, a prominent barrister, to represent me. Mr T Ryan, KC, announces that Mr Patrick Joseph Minahan and Mrs Minahan have retained him to represent me, stating they are friends of mine.

Mr Boyce objects. 'I am instructed that Mr Ryan has no authority to appear for Miss Partridge.'

'The question at issue is whether she is really capable of instructing anyone,' Mr Ryan replies.

'If she is not capable of instructing anyone, she is not capable of instructing you,' Mr Boyce argues.

The magistrate, Mr Charles Gale, addresses Mr Ryan. 'Before you go any further, I will have to be satisfied as to your standing to appear.'

Mr Boyce says he would like to cross-examine Mr Minahan on this point, suggesting that he had never seen Miss Partridge until that morning.

Mr Ryan quotes Section 6, sub-section 5, of the Lunacy Act, to the effect that any relative or friend might retain, or take, such person under his own care, if he satisfies the justices that such person would be properly taken care of.

'I have to be thoroughly satisfied. It is not a case to be rushed. It is a matter for medical opinion at present. Dr Ross and Dr Gibbs say they would like a remand for further observation. That is the position.'

Mr Boyce requests, 'If Miss Partridge is to be retained the officers should not allow her to be visited by anyone except those she wishes to see. Mrs Minahan visited her yesterday but Miss Partridge said she had not seen her in her life before and Miss Partridge does not want any visits by her again.'

The case is remanded for seven days.

'Mr Barton has offered to take you to Westbury, near Berry, along with his wife and daughter, for a little holiday and a rest, when this is over.' Mrs Touchell says, assuringly.

'What am I going to do without you, Mrs Touchell?'

'Keep yourself busy, dear child. Do your sewing. Keep your faith in God. The purity and beauty of your soul have filled me with astonishment. Your intelligence is wonderful and you are so affectionate.' Mrs Touchell seeks approval from the matron and removes her wristwatch. 'You can look after this until you are released. Take it as part of me. It is a treasured possession of mine. It may amuse you to hear it tick.'

Holding the watch close to my ear, I listen. 'It's like a needle tapping on glass, Mrs Touchell. Thank you … I will take good care of it.'

'The ticking is like a heartbeat as the Lord's fingers count the precious seconds in our lives.'

The uniformed nurse ushers me away and I hastily say goodbye to a dear, trusting friend.

Chapter Ten

Doctor Gibbs begins his examination the next day. He studies my notes aloud. 'Brigid Mary Partridge, Age: 28. Occupation: Teacher, Ex-nun. Born in Ireland. Address – late of Wagga. Religion: Roman Catholic …'

The medical certificate issued by Doctor Leahy is lying beside my file.

Doctor Gibbs is of slight build with a thin face and looking directly at me, he explains, 'A question mark hangs over the form of your mental disorder. Both Doctor Ross and I are Government Medical Officers. We will examine you for the next seven days to determine the nature of your illness.'

I escaped one institution only to be locked up in another. Here, the inhabitants are down-and-out and destitute and some patients are violent. Each day I am asked about my life both inside and outside the convent and doubts torment me that I may be held here forever. I am waking with headaches again and I pray that I will soon be free from the continual testing of my sanity.

'Your case is still receiving the public's attention,' Mrs Touchell says, bringing me daily newspapers with regular updates about 'The Escaped Nun'. Many letters, cards and telegrams are arriving from well-wishers and I receive them unopened and uncensored. I place them in a bundle in the drawer beside my bed and take great care to read each one. Mostly from women, they offer support, saying how wrong it is to 'lock up a nun'; some hope the conditions in Darlinghurst aren't as bad as is generally thought. One mentions that the screams of the inmates can be heard for miles around.

On Thursday, I am overjoyed when Doctor Ross informs me that himself and Doctor Gibbs are in agreement that they cannot find anything to indicate insanity and that I will be officially discharged tomorrow. My immediate plans are for a short holiday with Mr Barton and his wife and daughter while I await the arrival of Joseph from China. He will help to arrange my passage home. I am longing to return to Ireland, sharing the warmth of my family again but, more important, to be free from the chains that controlled me for so many years. I write to Mrs Touchell to thank her for her kindness and to ask if she could send on my white hat for my appearance at the Lunacy Court.

Darlinghurst, 12 August 1920

My dear Mrs Touchell

Accept my little letter in acknowledgement of your many kindnesses to me. Friends are multiplying every day; also letters, telegrams, and gifts, so you see, time is being whiled away for me. I am as happy as the day is long, and, please God, everything will soon be fixed up for the better. I would like you to send on my white hat, as the remark was in the papers last time, 'She had no hat on.' I have almost finished my sewing. You did not send me a pair of scissors but never mind now. I hope before another week is over to be quite settled again. Thank all kind friends for me for letters, etc. Hoping to see you soon, I remain your most loving friend.

B. M. Partridge

PS I hope to spend a few days more with you before I leave Australia. B.P.

I also write to the Bishop:

Darlinghurst, 12 August 1920

Your Lordship,

I don't blame you in the least for the false statement made. Worse has been said and proved otherwise. Father Barry was brought into it, too. I will explain later. I am too full of it. I have had a trying experience. All is well that ends well. Pray for your sincere child.

Brigid

On Friday morning, the reception house and the magistrate's small chambers are packed. Accompanied to my seat by a nurse, I can hear the large band of spectators that have gathered outside. They are a noisy crowd, goading each other. I seek out Mrs Touchell, who is faithfully at the side of the Reverend Touchell. She smiles back reassuringly.

Doctor Chisholm Ross is called: 'Doctor Gibbs and I examined Miss Partridge each day. In my opinion Miss Partridge is sane. I recommend her discharge.'

The magistrate officially announces, 'It having been recommended that the patient be discharged. I, therefore, discharge her immediately.' Almost everyone stands up and presses towards the court table. The nurse makes quickly for the door and ushers me through before anyone else can get to it. An order is given to close the door and allow no one to pass through while I am taken out the back entrance. For a couple of minutes the usual dignity of the court is overwhelmed by the excitement of those present, and a party feeling is decidedly in evidence.

The magistrate, in the midst of the hubbub, gives the order, 'Clear the court!'

I thank God it is over. But is it?

Outside, the jeering crowd is becoming more insulting as the police try to keep them back behind the railings. Listening from within the building, waiting for them to clear, I hear the Reverend William and Laura Touchell being besieged by journalists.

Mrs Touchell is saying, 'She came in a car from Wagga and had anything but a pleasant trip, dodging the people who were set to watch the roads. I cannot conceive how such a thin charge could possibly have been laid against her. And she, dear child – why her mind is so innocent and her attitude towards everybody is so kind that she can hardly understand such cruel charges. The idea that she is insane is absurd. Her intelligence is, believe me, above the ordinary.'

'Is the young girl staying at your home, Mrs Touchell?' a journalist probes.

'All I can tell you is she is staying with some of our friends. It seems best that she should not be worried. She wants a few days' rest and we think it advisable to maintain reticence on the matter. I know that she is in God's hands, but whether she is in the city or country I cannot tell you at present. Miss Partridge has frequently expressed a wish to go to her people in Ireland, but has said that, before any arrangements are made, she will wait for her brother who is on his way out to Sydney from China.'

Inspector Mitchell announces from the entrance steps that I have gone and the crowds melt away. Mr Barton and I are led out the back entrance to the mental hospital in Burton Street where we wait for a car to arrive. A short time later, a black car pulls up and hardly stops as we jump on board. It drives down Bourke Street at a speed perilously close to the legal limit.

'You need a complete rest, Miss Partridge. We will spend a fortnight in Berry along with my wife and daughter. It is a small village on the south coast surrounded by beaches with headlands and cliffs.'

'I cannot thank you enough, Mr Barton.' I tell him that he reminds me of my father who was born a Protestant but converted to my mother's religion on marriage. 'I left the convent with nothing and nowhere to go. You extended me a home and provided me with clothing, food and money. So many kind friends have rallied around, protecting and assisting me.'

'And we will continue to do so. It is a pleasure to meet and converse with you as you enjoy the freedom that has been yours since you broke away from the convent. It is hard to believe the publicity you are attracting. You are receiving greater coverage than the Anglo-Irish troubles.'

'I know little of the troubles in Ireland as we were not allowed newspapers in the convent and I worry about my family at home because my father was a British soldier. I am aware, though, of the public intrigue surrounding "The Escaped Nun".'

'It is deeper than that. The reason there is so much interest in your case is that I hold office as Grand Master of the Loyal Orange Lodge of New South Wales and the Orange Lodge Institution is taking an active part in it. The enmity between our two sides is rooted in history and religion. While you were held in remand in Darlinghurst, there was much rallying on your behalf. We were determined to gain you your liberty. Moral and financial support in abundance is at your disposal. The Victorian Protestant Federation Convention has congratulated the Loyal Orange Institution of New South Wales on its determination to stand by you. Mr James Robinson, who held office as Grand Worshipful Master before me, spoke on your behalf outside the Lunacy Court after your release.'

I feel disgusted at the action of the Church's champion (Mr Ryan) in absenting himself from the court proceedings this morning. This shows that the Church with all its boasting was afraid to cross swords with the worthy sons of the worthy sires who fought for victory. I never felt so proud of the Orange institution as I have today in successfully obtaining for others the liberty and rights that we claim for ourselves. I thoroughly enjoyed the depression that settled upon Mr Minahan.

The matter of further proceedings has not sufficiently developed for me at present to give any information that will reveal the position. Orangeism stands for light, liberty and truth, and has proved the value of those principles in connection with Miss Partridge.

'The Bishop charging me with being insane and issuing a warrant for my arrest was a stain on my character. I have written to him several times and have never received a reply. I was branded a lunatic and I want my name cleared before I return to Ireland.'

'You have our full support along with the support of all our members in whatever you decide.'

I realize the powerful influence Mr Barton holds, and I tell him I will have to await the arrival of Joseph from Hong Kong. *My future will depend on him.*

Chapter Eleven

At last, on 7 September, Joseph arrives in Sydney and Mr Barton is on his way to meet him to bring him back to Burwood where I am staying.

I gaze, disbelieving, at the outline in the doorway. 'Is it really you, Jody?' A bare whisper escapes my lips. His complexion is pale against his dark suit. He bends his head beneath the doorframe and removes his trilby, showing thick, black wavy hair and a strong, clean-cut face. A deep voice greets me, 'Bride,' and I tumble towards him. His brotherly arms are about my shoulders where I rest safely, breathing in the freshness of the cloth of his jacket. 'I am craving news of home. Please tell me about Mama and Dada, Susan, Kathleen and Lizzie.'

Keeping one arm tightly around my shoulder, he rummages through his jacket with the other. 'I have something here for you, Bride.' He lifts an envelope from his inside pocket and hands it to me, watching me anxiously open it. My eyes fall on seven small photographs and I seize them in my trembling fingers. 'Mama!' My breathing stops as I clasp her picture to my heart. I search for a handkerchief, sobbing softly. 'I remember every part of her, Jody. Her soft skin, smooth as satin, and the sweet scent of lavender from her hair as she kissed us goodnight.'

I look at Dada's picture. His steely stare is captured in a pose with his bushy white military moustache decorating his upper lip. 'Remember his habit of shaping and curling the ends of it upwards with his fingers until it resembled the handlebars of a bicycle?' I mimic the gesture and we both laugh. 'And here's Susan, her thick, brown hair swept up into a neat roll. She was about nineteen then.

Kathleen would have been fifteen years old. Her thin, impish face shows a bright smile. And here's sweet young Lizzie at fourteen. And here is a picture of you, Jody. You were just an eleven-year-old boy. How I have missed you all. Where have the years gone, Jody? I suppose you don't remember much about me?'

'I remember how my other sisters walked on to school without me while you waited behind.'

'I felt sorry for you because your school bag was bigger than you were.' I tell him, playfully.

' And how could I ever forget chasing you across The Curragh to pull your pigtails?'

Warmth flushes through me when he mentions home. 'Oh, Jody, I prayed you would come and take me back to Kildare.'

'That is why I am here. I will get you a passport as soon as I can.'

Mrs Barton knocks. Carrying a large silver tray laid out with a pot of tea, cups and saucers, she sets it down on the table. She had been so kind to me in Berry, taking me for walks along the coastal paths, and through nature forests, helping me recover from the unpleasantness of the charges laid against me. I have grown very fond of her. She leaves us alone to talk. The room is lit with afternoon sunshine as I enjoy a few peaceful hours with my brother and the recent unhappiness and grief is forgotten. We could easily be back at home, drinking tea and helping ourselves to cakes and biscuits. I study his fine features – the deep-set eyelids opening to show ice-blue eyes. I won't look away, lest he melts. Mr Barton offers him a bed for the night and we continue talking into the early hours.

Before he leaves the next day, I ask him when will he call again.

'A car will call for you tomorrow at 1.30 p.m. I have arranged for you to go with me to a private Catholic house.'

'I cannot leave tomorrow,' I blurt out quickly. 'I am meeting friends.' It is unbelievable that he wants to take me from my friends and place me with a Catholic family after all my efforts to avoid such a fate.

'I owe it to Mama and Dada to get to the bottom of all of this distasteful business. I am going up to Wagga to hear the Bishop's view of the case,' he says.

I plead with him to let me stay where I am until his return from Wagga. 'Why take me to strangers? I am comfortable here and do not wish to leave until I board the ship that will take me back to Ireland. Would you please enquire from the Bishop why I have never received the document dispensing me from my vows?'

He agrees and leaves. When he returns on Friday, his demeanour is changed. His arms are not about me and the air around us is cold. I wait for him to speak. His voice rises with a fierceness that is strange as he slams a piece of paper down on to the table in front of me. His change of mood frightens me and I wonder what has he been told during his visit to Wagga. 'This is the telegram I received from your Mother Superior. As soon as I received it, I threw up my position in Hong Kong and with the help of friends came to Sydney by the first steamer.'

COME AT ONCE: YOUR SISTER GONE MAD

A film of tears blur the words.

'Say something, Brigid. Explain yourself!'

I stand before him like a condemned prisoner. 'What do you want me to say, Joseph?'

'I want you to tell me what happened in the convent to make you suddenly leave in the way you did.'

'There was a misunderstanding over a sweeping brush and I walked to a nearby house. I asked could I wait there until the trouble had blown over. I meant no harm. I returned to the convent and was put to bed ... the doctor was sent for ... I was ordered to drink something. I was told it was castor oil, but it tasted vile ... A candle was lit at my bedside and I was ordered to lie still, and have a good sleep ... My arms were placed crosswise on my breast and holy water was sprinkled about my body. I thought it was my deathbed.'

'And that's what planted the nonsensical idea in your head that you were being poisoned?'

'I knew my disobedience would be severely punished.' My tear-soaked handkerchief crumples in my hand as I beg him to understand. 'I watched my chance, swallowed some soap suds and vomited the drink I had been given … I got out through a window in my night attire and went to a nearby house.'

'Barefoot, in your nightgown, in the dark?' he sneers. 'Is it any wonder they thought you were mad?'

'I am not mad, Joseph! My sanity has been tested and proved in the Lunacy Court. I ran away because I was unhappy. I had been enclosed in a convent for almost twelve years and did not know what to do.'

'It was the life you chose. It was *your* sacrifice.'

'Tell, me something, Joseph. You wanted to be a priest; why did you abandon *your* studies?'

He stiffens, stepping back abruptly. I jolt at this change in him, the impatience in his voice. 'I left in the proper manner. How dare you try to compare me to the shameful way you left? How did you get involved with the people you are staying with?'

'I had nobody in the convent in whom I could confide. When I fled, I had to throw myself on the mercy of strangers for protection. They gave me refuge in their home.' I cannot read the expression on his face. Has he listened to anything I have said? 'Is it because they are Protestants? Dada was a Protestant.'

Veins swell on his forehead as he holds a tight fist in the air, shouting, 'Your Mother Superior informs me that the people you are with are not ordinary Protestants! Barton is the Grand Master of the Orange Lodge, the enemy of our faith!' His fist comes down heavily on to the table.

I cower beneath him, pressing my hands over my ears, not wanting to listen to the cruel words against those who had come to my aid.

'Please, Jody, keep your voice down. They will hear you.'

'Are you aware of the sectarianism you are stirring up? I have already witnessed a widening gap at home between the two sides as the Irish Catholics struggle for their independence from British rule. It has caused much trouble too for Mama and Dada. Did you know that Mama's family won't speak to her because she is married to a Protestant British soldier? I was informed during my trip to Wagga that the same depth of division is rising up here, sparked by *you*.'

'I am not interested in the stirrings of sectarianism. These people respected my wish to abandon religious life. I left the convent with nothing, no clothes, no shoes and no money. All that I carried were the scars of convent life. I had nowhere to go. My biggest fear was that I would be taken back. Mr Barton arranged a home for me with the Reverend William Touchell and his wife, Laura.'

'Mr Barton! Mr Barton! These people are only interested in you to further their own cause,' he shouts before leaving abruptly. He returns the next day still wishing to place me with a Catholic family.

The Bartons and the Touchells do their best to dissuade him. 'Your sister sees the "Romish Church" as her enemy now,' explains Mr Touchell.

'As you know, I am a Catholic and my sister wishes to retain her faith, and I don't like you talking about my church like that.' He strides to the front door, slamming it behind him.

I tell Mrs Touchell that his visits only serve to infuriate me. I cannot conceal my panic. 'He has mentioned more than once that he wants to take me to a Catholic family. I don't want to see him again. My head is paining me. I will have to lie down.'

'You are trembling. I will call the doctor, Brigid. He will prescribe something.'

I am again in need of protection – this time it is from my own brother.

★★★

Joseph returns the next day and is told that I am receiving medical attention for an illness caused by his actions. 'If you promise that you will not exercise your influence in the interests of your sister's religion, you will be permitted to see her,' Mrs Touchell says.

'The demand for such a guarantee from me, her brother, is impudent and unnecessary.'

Listening from another room, I hear his pleas. 'I am the only blood relation my sister has in this part of the world. She is entirely innocent in worldly affairs and I consider it inhuman that she is not delivered into my care.'

I almost feel sorry for him. I want to trust him and agree to speak with him.

'When you first visited me, Joseph, I did promise to go with you to another house, but a Catholic family will force me back into the convent.'

'I can assure you, Brigid, that far from the nuns trying to get you back, no convent will take you in.'

His words cut me like a sword. I look into his pitiless eyes. When had he become so bitter?

'I am not so green that I don't see why you continually go from the Bishop to a "friend's" house and then to me. I have a good home and can stay here for as long as I please. I have made up my mind to stay with the friends I am with until I am in a fit state of health to travel. They will see to my passage and they won't leave me without friends to take care of me on the way. There is nobody interfering with my religion. I can go to Mass from here as from elsewhere as others do. I am very much run down. I am under medical care at present and wish to be left alone to regain my strength.'

Before he leaves, I tell him I am reluctant to see him again.

Searching for understanding, I turn to the Touchells. 'He looked upon the charge of lunacy brought against me as a mere nothing and my being hunted from one house to another as of no consequence.'

'Your brother does not know very much about the Orange Institution. It is not an enemy of the Christian faith or of the country in which it is permitted to exist, and it is not an enemy of liberty for everybody, irrespective of their religious beliefs. It was Orangemen and women who assisted you in making good your escape from the convent. We had expected him to be as much moved by your story as we have been,' says the Reverend Touchell, his voice filled with compassion.

'But, sadly, he has listened to the biased story of others,' I say. 'He did not express one word of resentment at the act which led to my arrest and subsequent appearance in the Lunacy Court and imprisonment for several days, neither did he show the least feeling in that regard. He dismissed my story of alleged poisoning with contempt. He said that I should be delivered into his charge. I am a free agent, seven years older than him, and am capable of determining my own future actions. By what right, may I ask, does he demand that I be delivered into his care?'

The Catholic Federation, acting on behalf of Bishop Dwyer, takes charge of Joseph, making use of him to gain publicity in its campaign against Barton and Touchell, who they accuse of detaining me against my will.

★★★

The Catholic Press appeals on Joseph's behalf on 16 September 1920.

In order to enable Joseph Partridge to use every possible legal means to free his sister from people who deliberately lay themselves out to ruin her soul and, afterwards, to help him take her to their relatives in Ireland, a sum of money is needed. Christian freedom will contribute to a fund with this worthy object. Small donations from many people will show the strength of public feeling on the matter. The process of law may be costly, but those who would protect our devoted Sisterhoods from wanton insult and who resent an impudent outrage on a nerve-racked girl, will, we are sure, add their tributes. All amounts sent to Mr C. Lawlor, General Secretary, Catholic Federation, 197 Castlereigh Street, Sydney, will be acknowledged.

Joseph is being paraded like a show puppy. He does not seem to know he is being fooled and being made a tool by others. He says he wants to take me away, but every time he talks of it, he mentions a different place to take me to. He tells me he learned from the Bishop that I was not free from my vows and that I would have to see the

Bishop who would give me dispensation. I am done with convent life for good. Joseph's visits and hostile manner have strengthened my resolve and I have written to him telling him that I am amongst friends and that Mr and Mrs Touchell have asked me to stay with them until I become strong again. I will then decide for myself what I will do in future.

Mr Barton tells me that every member of the Loyal Orange Lodge in New South Wales is behind me to have the stain cast on my character removed. 'If you give your consent, we will issue a writ claiming at least £5,000 damages for malicious prosecution and wrongful arrest. If you say 'Go', no time will be lost in our endeavour to secure for you that measure of justice, to which we, and a great section of the public, think you are entitled.'

I cannot take on the Bishop without taking on the Catholic Church and I cannot do it alone.

★★★

Two months later, Mr Barton, and the Reverend William and Laura Touchell accompany me to Sydney, where we are introduced to Mr Alexander Shand, a leading Sydney barrister and King's Counsellor. I am told he is renowned for his willingness to accept difficult and often seemingly impossible briefs.

Mr Barton sets a bundle of newspapers on the desk. 'Each one of these contains false statements that are damaging to this young lady's reputation. The Bishop of Wagga, Doctor Joseph Dwyer's actions played a pivotal role in the extraordinary hubbub that followed her disappearance from the convent. His actions set a legal process in motion whereby a warrant was issued for her arrest. When the news-hungry press got hold of the story, she was hunted about the country like an outlaw as the police searched for her in every state in Australia and New Zealand. Finally, she suffered the harrowing experience of being arrested and sent to a madhouse to have her sanity tested. She was branded a lunatic and now she wants her name cleared before she returns to Ireland.'

'The Bishop's remedy is a simple one,' says Mr Touchell, 'as

Christian as it is simple – namely, one word of sympathy.'

'Miss Partridge, you ask only for an apology from the Bishop and your solicitor has written to him several times,' says Mr Shand. 'So far, not a word of sympathy has come to you, from the time of your discharge from the Lunacy Court up to date.' Picking up one of the newspapers, he continues, 'Much has been made of "The Missing Nun Story". It will not be an easy case. An ex-nun taking on the Roman Catholic Church?'

'But Miss Partridge is not on her own. She has the full support of the Loyal Orange Institution in New South Wales and all its members,' Mr Barton affirms.

'We will have to prove that Bishop Dwyer acted with malice. Did he desire to cause you harm or suffering when he laid an information against you?' Mr Shand searches for his notebook. 'Miss Partridge, please begin by telling me about your twelve years as a nun at Mount Erin Convent, Wagga, up until the time of your incarceration.'

Chapter Twelve

Newspapers continue to feed the public's cravings with the upcoming Court Case, delivering hot news straight from the presses. And now, Sydney is waiting for a glimpse of the young woman accorded something akin to fame when she was thrown into the spotlight a year ago. On Thursday, 30 June 1921, the city wakes to the first day of the trial. The streets, splashed with overnight rain, spring to life early as people hasten towards the Supreme Court to join the lengthening queues of inquisitive onlookers converging on to King Street. Not only are they crowding the roads and footpaths, but also all available windows and balconies in the immediate vicinity of Elizabeth Street and King Street. Every possible space is occupied.

While I am caught up in the preparations for the trial, Mrs Touchell remains at my side as a faithful companion, assuring me that I have a strong and genuine case. But I often relapse into panic when I am alone. My family has never seemed so far away. I wonder will Joseph attend court.

Absorbed in my own fears, I am unaware how much an ex-nun suing her Bishop has excited the imagination of the public. I am shocked at the multitudes queuing outside the Georgian-style courthouse. I hear later that the numbers that gathered on that first morning were unprecedented in the history of the law courts. Policemen guarding the iron gates are trying to keep the footpaths as clear as possible to allow me and my small group of supporters to have free access into the imposing temple of oak panelling and Corinthian columns where I will spend the days of the trial.

I grip Mrs Touchell's arm as we are directed to Jury Court No 5 where someone is already waiting to guide us to a table set apart for

Counsel. The reassuring presence of the Reverend Mr Touchell and Mr Barton on my other side helps me walk with confidence into the packed courtroom. Mr Shand, dressed in his black gown and white wig, is seated beside F S Boyce and P R Higgins assisting. All three are almost hidden behind a mound of books.

'The Bishop is here, seated along with his counsel,' says Mrs Touchell, turning her head quickly and discreetly to check who is with him. From newspaper reports, we know he is to be represented by Scotland-born James Lang Campbell, KC, with George Flannery KC and Allan Victor Maxwell, assisting. I long to look around, to stare squarely into the face of this man who has so carelessly set about destroying my reputation, but I am afraid I will falter before his stern gaze. In the convent, his authority is supreme, almost God-like, and those years of servitude have left their mark on me. If he was trying to avoid a public scandal for the nuns and the Holy Church, why did he react in the way he did, making untrue allegations against me?

The indignation and hurt that triggered my decision to challenge the Bishop are beset by fears that I may lose the case. The habit of waking early remains from my convent days and every morning I pray silently in the small hours for the strength to withstand the questioning I will face throughout the trial. I am overwhelmed by a sudden urge to run from the courthouse and hide from all that is about to unfold. It is too late to run anywhere. I asked for an apology from the man who labelled me insane. It was not forthcoming. Events have been set in motion and there is nothing I can do but place my trust in my own sense of righteousness and the legal advice I have received. I am calmed by the steady presence of Mrs Touchell and the Reverend William Touchell, along with Mr Barton and others who have not only given me protection since I fled the convent but have offered their wholehearted financial support to help clear my name and the slur cast upon my character by the Bishop's actions.

The court bailiff wrenches me from my thoughts as he calls out, 'All stand.'

Judge Ferguson, dressed in his ceremonial robe, takes his place on the bench. His fair complexion is waxen beneath his snowy-white wig. He studies his packed courtroom and, deciding everyone is in place, pecks his gavel lightly. The whispering ceases. Mr Shand has told me that the judge's knowledge of the law relating to evidence and procedure places him high among the most distinguished judges to have sat upon the bench. I draw comfort from this fact, but I am in an environment dominated by men who could, through lack of understanding and the cold certainty of male supremacy, decide that I had rightly been judged to be insane simply because I was forced to leave a life that had become unendurable. The feeling that I had no vocation was growing stronger within me but the simplest solution – to ask for a dispensation of my vows – did not suggest itself.

Mr Shand rises for the opening address. 'The plaintiff is a young lady named Brigid Mary Partridge, and the defendant, Joseph Wilfred Dwyer.' He begins detailing the grounds of the action.

'That the defendant appeared before a justice of the peace and falsely and maliciously and without reasonable or probable cause, informed the justice on oath that the plaintiff was a person deemed to be insane and was without sufficient means of support.' He outlines the charges. 'Bishop Dwyer had caused her to be apprehended and brought before a stipendiary magistrate, caused her imprisonment for medical observation, whereby she was prevented from attending to her affairs and had incurred expense defending herself from his charge of insanity.' He continues, 'Bishop Dwyer denies the charges … he did not by virtue of the warrant, cause or procure the plaintiff's arrest, imprisonment or remand.'

I force myself to concentrate on these opening statements. Here it is at last – my case laid out in public. The legal language is far removed from my own outraged, confused and panicked reaction to all that unfolded on the night I ran from the convent.

'Miss Partridge is the daughter of a Protestant father and a Catholic mother. Her people live in Ireland, and she came to Australia in 1909. She was then a young girl, eighteen years of age, and without worldly experience. She was attracted by the promises that religion gave.'

Mr Shand urges the jury to ignore the publicity the case has already received. 'This is,' he stresses, 'simply an ordinary case between two citizens who are supposed to enjoy the same privileges under the law.'

He asks, 'Did Bishop Dwyer act within his lawful rights or did he take advantage of his position in the community when he swore an information that Brigid Mary Partridge was deemed to be insane? Bishop Dwyer had not gone to the local office in Wagga to sign out his warrant. Was that because the unusual action of a nun running away from her convent would have been known to too many of the residents? Instead, ten days after Miss Partridge had left the convent, he chose to go to a magistrate in Sydney to swear that she was deemed to be insane and without visible means of support, after she had told him by letter that she had left the convent.'

I exchange a glance with Mrs Touchell and she gives me a warm smile. Her kindness has supported me throughout, giving me the strength to face this trial.

'The Bishop's object was this,' insists Mr Shand, 'he wanted to get hold of her. He was not concerned simply with her welfare, but he believed she was in the hands of heretics, and he wanted to get her out of those hands, and he was prepared to go to any length, even to having her arrested in the way she was arrested, and getting her under the influences which would bring her back to the convent.'

Mr Shand refers to a letter Bishop Dwyer wrote to Mrs Thompson saying that he had acted entirely against his own letter and caused the girl's arrest. If he had acted without reasonable cause, or for some religious purpose, or some indirect motive, he was responsible for the consequences of his act.

Mr Shand states, 'Money is not the object of this young lady. She wants to clear her character against the stigma that has been cast on it by the proceedings in lunacy. She had been branded here for days and weeks as a person whose mind was so unstable that she had to be arrested in the middle of the night, taken to the Reception House, remanded, and ultimately brought before the court and discharged. Before this action was taken, she wanted to have her name and her sanity established by the man who had made the charge against her. She wrote to him, through her solicitor, and asked him to apologize to her and admit that this action of his had been taken without justification.'

Looking straight at the four jury men, Mr Shand says, 'If we can establish a case, then I submit that this defendant should be subjected to such substantial damages as will vindicate the name of this lady and compensate her for the wrong she has suffered by reason of the Bishop's action.'

When my name is called, I rise slowly and uncertainly from the hard wooden seat, striving to compose myself. I feel the discomfort of every pair of eyes in the courtroom fastened on my back when I begin the lonely walk to the witness box. With my heels rattling across the polished floor, I pass the press who are there in force, not just the local press, but also those representing the whole of the Commonwealth, recording the proceedings for the news-hungry public. Court artists are busy sketching every scene, capturing every blink and twitch with the skillful use of their charcoal pencils. It is ironic. I had chosen to live my life in seclusion and I am now in the full glare of the world. The Bible is unsteady in my hands and my mouth is too dry to speak. The air in the courtroom stills as listening ears strain to hear my voice. I clear my throat before quietly repeating, 'I, Brigid Partridge, do swear by Almighty God that the evidence I shall give will be the truth, the whole truth and nothing but the truth.'

I have an unrestricted view of the courtroom and avoid looking towards the Bishop, focussing instead on the expressionless faces of the men seated in the jury box. Three are silver-haired, and the fourth, the youngest one, is showing signs of approaching baldness. I am here because of the actions of one authoritative man. My decision to challenge his depiction of me is to be judged by these four men, who will, I fervently hope, be fair and compassionate. Can everyone inside the room hear my heart beating against my chest? My palms grow clammy and I set my hands into my lap to steady them. I begin with an account of my life in the convent.

'The order is known as an enclosed order, members not being allowed outside the convent grounds where the cemetery for the sisters is situated. We were only allowed newspapers containing anything judged to be of educational interest to the schoolchildren, but our letters were always censored, except those arriving for one of the sisters on her feast day.'

His Honour says, 'You will need to speak up, Miss Partridge, so the whole court can hear you.'

I raise my voice to continue. 'Letters we wrote were handed in unsealed and it was only by consent that we could communicate with anyone outside. I had no relatives or friends who visited me. I was teaching for six months at the branch convent at Lockhart and was subsequently transferred to Ganmain convent where I taught for five and a half years. In 1918, when I was at Wagga on vacation, I was asked by the Reverend Mother to take charge of the refectory, normally the work of a lay sister. I did this work for two years.'

'What was your state of health during that time?' Mr Shand asks.

'Very poor. I felt very much run down for fully eight months before I left.'

'Did you complain?'

'Yes. I asked the Reverend Mother for a tonic.'

'You went on doing your work?'

'Yes, till the day I left. Two or three times I told the Mother Superior that I was worn out. Sister Margaret, the porteress, was dying, and I had to do her work, as well as that in the refectory. It did not leave me with a moment, so I asked the Reverend Mother to be sent back to teaching, but she said she was short of lay nuns, and I would have to stay on. The housework did not agree with my health as there was too much of it.'

How can I explain to the jury the work I had to do in a day? There were nearly eighty nuns in the convent. I washed and dried their dishes, scoured and cleaned after them, polished floors and prepared vegetables and potatoes for them. My back and shoulders ached, my feet swelled and blisters scarred my hands. I was constantly tired and run down. All I can do in this courtroom is list my daily timetable beginning at five a.m. and ending at ten p.m. and hope that the jury, all men, will somehow understand.

'You know it is the practice of the Bishop to visit the convent to interview the individual members of the community with the object of finding out whether they are happy or have any complaints?'

'Yes, once a year.'

'Now, three questions are always put on those occasions, namely as to your health, whether you have any complaints, and as to whether you are perfectly happy?' In regard to the second question: "Have you any complaints to make to me as Bishop?" what did you answer?'

'I answered no, simply because I had to.'

Laughter erupts in the courtroom.

★★★

There was no laughter when I sat scared and tongue-tied before Bishop Dwyer a year ago. I had practised what I would say over and over only to be ordered by the Mother Superior not to speak of any grievances. I had felt a longing to break through his cold demeanour and express my feelings truthfully when he asked those three questions about my life in the convent. The interview had been a dutiful two-minute exercise to be ticked off when completed. His lack of interest in anything I had to say was highlighted when he spent more time ministering to the needs of the convent plants. He knew no more about me when it was over than he knew before it began. Yet, within two months, he would swear an oath that I was insane.

★★★

Coming to Saturday, 24 July, the day you left the convent, can you tell the court what happened?'

'There was a dispute about a broom. One of the other sisters told an untruth, and I was blamed for it. I went out the back way and went to Mrs Burgess' house, which was about ten minutes from the convent and stayed there until about a quarter to five.' I tell the court what happened when I went back and what made me run away the second time.

82

'What were you clad in?'

'My nightdress.'

'I understand your sole desire was to get away from the convent?'

'Yes, and I thought that if I went back to get my clothes I would never get a chance to get away again.'

★★★

At last, lunchtime arrives and I am relieved to step down from the witness box. Mrs Touchell takes my arm and we are barely through the door when a disturbance occurs, adding to the trauma of the day. A young man pushes through the crowd, grabbing my arm.

'Joseph!' I cry out at the force of him pulling me away from Mrs Touchell.

Unable to contain his anger he suddenly swings around and rushes at Mrs Touchell.

'What in God's name are you doing, Joseph?' The older woman would have fallen if a nearby man had not caught her in time.

Joseph tries to frogmarch me along the corridor leading on to King Street but I pull free from his grip. Two men in the crowd have noticed the attack and join in the fray, knocking Joseph to the ground. For a terrifying instant it seems I will be overwhelmed by the curiosity of the swaying mob. To my relief, Sergeant Mills and three of his constables arrive and order the crowd to move on.

Women back cautiously away while Joseph rises unsteadily to his feet. The police, assisted by court officials, eventually restore order and hustle the combatants out into King Street.

Joseph adjusts the collar and tie that are almost torn from his neck. Mrs Touchell, embarrassed and upset, accompanies me to the other end of the corridor. Protected by Mr Touchell and Mr Barton, we move out of the view of the spectators. But Joseph is still determined to speak to me. With the permission of the deputy sheriff he is allowed to sit with me, along with Mr and Mrs Touchell and Mr Barton, while we take our lunch in one of the witness rooms.

His attitude towards my friends has clearly not changed when I ask him to apologize to Mrs Touchell, and he refuses. 'Had it not been for the help offered by these good people, I might have been locked up in a government asylum forever, with no one ever knowing about it.' Ashamed and angered, I try to equate his behaviour with the young boy I had known before I left home. When had he become so harsh and judgemental? Why did he believe he had the authority to manhandle me? Little is spoken during the strained luncheon.

★★★

My evidence resumes after lunch, giving my account of getting away from Wagga.

Concluding for the day, Mr Shand asks, 'Did anyone offer you support while you were outside the convent?'

'Mrs Thompson at Wagga, Mrs Burgess, Mrs Touchell and Mr Barton all asked me to remain with them.'

'Was there anything in the Order you objected to?'

'I was dissatisfied with my life.'

Chapter Thirteen

Black skies bubbling over Sydney are no deterrent to the swelling numbers that gather under a forest of umbrellas outside the Supreme Court for the second day of the trial. Young newsboys, carrying bundles of newspapers filled with accounts of yesterday's proceedings, are running up and down the long line of people shouting the headlines.

A report in *The Sun* makes me smile.

> *All eyes fell on the young lady, whose age was given as thirty. She looked ten years younger. Her clear skin and pink complexion could be compared to that of a child, her baby blue eyes accentuating her youthful appearance. She wore a long coat over her dark suit and her brown hair was tied up beneath the dark velvet hat that covered her head. Her physique was slight but she was above medium height.*

Sergeant Mills, who came to my aid yesterday during the fracas with Joseph, greets me with a smile. 'You don't know how famous you are, Miss Partridge. People are offering me money to help get them a seat in the crowded gallery.' His light-hearted banter lifts the heavy atmosphere. Only a faint glow of light shows the scene in the gloom of a wintry day. A dampening smell pervades the air carried in by those afforded the privilege of finding a precious seat in the little gallery or among the portions of the floor set apart for the general public.

I wait in the witness box for cross-examination to begin, hoping the court artists don't capture the fear I feel within. The Bishop is seated immediately behind his counsel and I avert my eyes to avoid his gaze. I look around for Joseph, but cannot see him.

Mr Campbell, for the defence, rises from his seat and asks me about the people who offered their support when I ran away. He questions me about Mr Barton, asking did I know why he took so much interest in me? I told him I had made friends of the people I had gone to.

'You knew that he was the Grand Master of the Orange Lodge?'

'Yes.'

'Did he explain to you how he came to know of your existence and situation?'

'He had heard it through others.'

'You knew that the police surrounded Thompson's house, and you say they turned the searchlight on it?'

'Yes.'

'You heard the Thompsons deny to the police that you were in the house?'

'Yes.'

'Yet you allowed these people to search on a winter's night for you?'

'They knew I was not wandering about.'

'You had been failing in health for two years before this unfortunate day?'

'Yes.'

'The other sisters complained of your wakefulness, didn't they?'

'Yes.'

'Your relations with the other sisters were all right up to this time, were they not?'

'It was not very kind when I had to sleep on the verandah for a year.'

'I am asking you whether your relations were friendly?'

'Yes, they were.'

The chains of unwavering obedience and loyalty to my fellow sisters are not so easily broken and I cannot speak of the ill will of any of them.

'You knew, did you not, that if you desired to leave the convent you had a perfect right to do so?'

'Yes. I know you are supposed to ask for dispensation.'

'Did you know that the procedure was to go before the superior and that if the superior refused you had the right of appeal to a higher authority: the Bishop?'

'Yes.'

'You know also that if you have any complaint to make about the superior of the convent or anyone else there the Bishop is the person to whom that complaint should be made?'

'Yes.'

'And you have free right of communication with him, not only on the occasions of his periodical visits, but it is open to you at all times to make any complaints to him if you desire to do so?'

'Yes. If the Reverend Mother agrees.'

'Do you know that if you write to the Bishop no one in the convent has any right to interfere with your correspondence?'

'No, I did not.'

'You will admit that you took no steps towards informing the Bishop of your dissatisfaction and your desire to be free from it?'

'I knew quite well it would be very hard.'

'Did you ever give any hint to the Mother Superior?'

'I told her several times I was not as happy as I would wish to be, but I did not tell her I was going to leave.'

'I am afraid very few of us are as happy as we would wish to be! Did you really mean that the Mother Superior would visit upon you any cruelty or any course of punishment if you told the Bishop you were not contented and happy?'

'Yes, she would have made it very unpleasant for me.'

'And would punish you for it?'

'Yes, in some way. I would be told that it was a temptation if I asked to leave, and then be asked to pray.'

Rarely raising his voice beyond a monotonous tone, Mr Campbell pursues the allegation of poisoning ... 'Coming to the night of 24 July, the occasion on which you said the doctor gave you medicine to poison you and the nuns at the convent had prepared your deathbed, you say it was poison, don't you?'

'I thought it was.'

His Honour: 'At the time?'

'When I drank it. I think now that it was a sleeping draught for some further ill-treatment for running away.'

'That you were to be sent asleep and then tortured in your sleep?'

'Ill-treated.'

'By whom?'

'By the sisters.'

'You have already stated that the ladies in the convent showed you nothing but kindness?'

'Not always,' I reply, unable to forget the two years I spent as a lay sister.

'Whom did you suspect were implicated in this monstrous desire to murder you?'

'Sister Brendan, the Mother Superior and the doctor.'

'Did you tell anybody about the poisoning?'

'I told Mrs Thompson and thought that if she felt it necessary to mention it she could do so.'

'You were under certain religious vows, were you not?'

'Yes.'

'Do you regard those vows as binding on you in respect to the Bishop?'

'They are always binding.'

'You know that the necessary decree freeing you from your vows has been made?'

'I have no information about that.'

'Did your brother not tell you that he had received notification that you were free from your vows?'

'My brother told me so, but the document was not given to me.'

'It was arranged with Mrs Thompson to give no information as to your whereabouts?'

'I expressed a wish that no information should be given as to my whereabouts.'

'That included the police, of course.'

'I suppose so.'

'Just one more question … Did you think you had the right to leave the convent without the consent of the Bishop and be a free citizen?'

'Not before I left.'

'I have no more questions, Your Honour.'

★★★

This concludes my evidence. I leave the witness box at 3.20 p.m., having been under examination for seven-and-a-half hours.

When the court rises for the day I am held back for ten minutes to avoid a crowd that has gathered in St James's Place. Instead, I am escorted through the main doors into King Street and a waiting car.

Chapter Fourteen

With a break over the weekend, droves of people are lured back to the courthouse on Monday morning. A lengthy queue, with more females than males, has again formed in King Street long before eight a.m. and increases in length as time goes on. The women are there to support me in a male-dominated world where women have no decision-making power.

At about ten minutes to ten the King Street gates and the doors are thrown open and the waiting crowd files in, quickly filling the gallery of the court. A halt is then called, and the remainder of the long queue, having been informed that there is no room for any more, quietly move away, their faces filled with disappointment at their bad luck in having been so far away from the entrance in the first instance.

Sergeant Mills greets us with a warm smile. 'Good morning, Miss Partridge. You're as popular as ever after the weekend. The police officers are having sad tales poured into their ears by women who have journeyed miles to hear your case.' His words buoy me up for another day of legal proceedings.

One of the jury submits a request for increased fees. Mr Justice Ferguson readily concurs and each member of the jury is to get an additional guinea a day.

I am recalled and His Honour asks whether I had seen the letter written by the Bishop to Mr and Mrs Thompson.

'I have not seen it. I had left the residence of Mr and Mrs Thompson when the letter arrived and it was sent back.'

I resume my place as a spectator at the rear of my counsel to listen to the evidence of the first witness.

James Christopher Farley, the sergeant of police at No 1 station says that on 4-5 August he received an order for the apprehension of Brigid Mary Partridge from his superior officer. At about midnight on 7 August, he went to the house of the Reverend W Touchell at Kogarah, and was introduced to Miss Partridge. 'I obtained her full name and the fact that her relatives were all in Ireland.'

Mrs Touchell squeezes my hand. How could we ever forget all those police officers arriving on the doorstep?

'I asked Miss Partridge why she left the Wagga Convent, and she said that she had had some trouble there and it could not be rectified. She went on to say that if she had got into communication with Bishop Dwyer things would probably have been all right. She asked why he was making all the fuss, saying she had already sent in her resignation. If he accepted it, everything would, she remarked, be all right.'

Continuing, he says, 'After I read the order to her, she asked me why could I not leave it until the following Monday morning. It was then Saturday. If I would leave it until Monday she would meet me anywhere I liked, as she had no intention of flouting the law. I said I could not do that, as my orders were to take her to the Reception House. She asked if a friend could accompany her and, on my agreeing, Mrs Touchell came with her in a motor car. She said that when she went back to the convent something happened which determined her to leave the convent for good and all. I did not ask what happened. I arrested her on the authority of the order given me. During the two hours I was with her she did not show any weakness of mind. She was a little nervous at first, but after a minute or two became quite calm and collected.'

'Was she searched?' Mr Shand asks.

'I asked her if she had any valuables on her, and she put some things –'

Mr Campbell stands up. 'This is quite irrelevant.'

Mr Shand says he will not bother with it, adding, 'It was merely an act of indignity.'

Next, my counsel calls upon the medical testimony of Doctor Eric Tivey.

He says he went to Mrs Thompson's house on 25 July between 7 and 8 a.m., having received a telephone message from her sister, Miss Heathwood. Accompanied by the inspector of police and a constable, he was asked to examine Miss Partridge.

'How was her manner?' asks Mr Shand.

'Her manner appeared to be perfectly normal. She was quite possessed and her answers were given with decision. There was no inconsequential talk, and she made no accusations against the convent.'

'You were examining her for her sanity?'

'That was my object.'

'And what conclusions did you come to?'

'In my opinion she was quite sane at the time I saw her. There was no evidence of insanity.'

'Supposing you had known that this lady had left the convent without permission and had gone back with the sisters; had been ordered to bed … and that she had come to the conclusion that an attempt had been made to poison her. If you had known this, would you have altered your opinion?'

'I consider that the state of fear that would be induced would be quite sufficient to make her think that an attempt was being made to punish her for what she must have regarded as a very wrong action.'

'Was there anything in her physical condition that would prevent her from earning her living?'

'I could find nothing.'

'You did not prescribe for her?'

'No.'

In reply to further questions Doctor Tivey agrees that Doctor Leahy, having knowledge of my earlier history, and having seen me on the night of the 24th, might be in a better position to judge of the significance of my acts than anyone else. So far as Doctor Tivey could remember, the letter I had written within an hour or so of him having seen me made no reference to persecution.

★★★

Mr Campbell takes up the questioning: 'Do you say that an accusation of having been poisoned is not evidence of delusion as to persecution?'

'Her state of mind may have been brought about by fear of retribution, which may have arisen from the acts of being put to bed and the sprinkling of holy water in such a way as is only done in cases of impending death.'

'At the time you saw the plaintiff did you know Doctor Leahy had expressed the opinion, after she had left the convent, that she was insane?'

'I think I had heard that Doctor Leahy had seen her, but I cannot recollect definitely whether any statement was expressed of his view of her mental condition before or after I went to Thompson's place.'

'Did you have a conversation with Doctor Leahy himself about the condition of the sister?'

'No, I did not see Doctor Leahy at that time.'

'Knowing that Doctor Leahy had had the plaintiff under treatment and that he was acquainted with her medical history, did you refer to Doctor Leahy in connection with the case at all – if not, why not?'

'No, and for this reason: under the terms of the Lunacy Act a patient must be medically examined by two medical men separately and independently of one another, and for that reason I was prevented from conferring with Doctor Leahy.'

'When you saw the Reverend Mother did she say, "We cannot allow her to go away to people we do not know anything about. We are responsible to her parents for her?"'

'Yes.'

'The Reverend Mother appeared anxious for the safety of the plaintiff?'

'She was greatly concerned. I do not know whether it was because of her safety or because she had erred.'

'Then you drew no inference from the fact of the plaintiff having left in the manner she did at night, no inference that she was concerned for her safety?'

'I have not the slightest idea what concerned her most.'

Mr Shand asks a final question. 'Have you any reason now for changing the opinion you expressed before when you saw the girl and said she was sane?'

'No, no reason.'

At the close of Doctor Tivey's cross-examination, he expresses a wish to be allowed to return to Wagga. Before granting permission, His Honour asks the jury whether there are any questions they desire to ask.

The foreman rises and asks Doctor Tivey whether, notwithstanding that he (Doctor Tivey) had already declared that the plaintiff was perfectly sane at the time he examined her, from a medical point of view, would it be possible for the plaintiff to have been insane even for one day?

'In my opinion it would have been impossible.'

That concludes his evidence and from the agility with which he steps from the witness box and the smile that wreathes his face as he hurriedly makes his exit, he is not sorry that the ordeal of a searching cross-examination is over.

This is the end of proceedings for another day and at four o'clock the police adopt a ruse in Elizabeth Street. A motorcar is drawn up near the back entrance to the court and in it is an officer who seems anxiously waiting for someone. A number of policemen are also close by and the word goes round that I will leave by that car. A crowd of about two hundred quickly assembles, but they are deceived, for I leave by the St James's Road entrance where only about twenty persons are on the lookout.

Chapter Fifteen

On Tuesday, we arrive at the court at 9.30 and gain admittance to the yard at the rear of the Bankruptcy and No 2 Equity Courts, where, by pre-arrangement, Mr Barton, Mrs Touchell and I pose before newspaper cameras. This is the fourth day of the hearing and, again, it is predominantly women who crowd into the gallery. I follow the case easily from my seat behind my counsel.

Mr Shand calls the next witness. The sturdy figure of William Alexander Duprez, Inspector of Police stationed at Wagga, steps into the witness box to begin his evidence.

'I was on leave prior to retirement. I have been in the police force for thirty-three years, five of which were spent at Wagga.'

'What was the first you knew of the plaintiff being out of the convent?'

'I was told of it on Sunday morning, 25 July 1920. Sergeant O'Rourke reported it before going off duty. He said one of the sisters had got away from the convent in her night clothes and stated that he had sent Constable Brownlow to make inquiries. He and another constable had searched for her all night, even in the waterholes. Later on, Brownlow reported that the girl had been taken in by the Thompsons, who, however, denied that she was there.'

'Are the Thompsons well-known and reputable people in Wagga?'

'Yes, as far as I know.'

At Mr Shand's request, Inspector Duprez relates the interview he had with Bishop Dwyer on 27 July, when the Bishop called at his office. The Bishop said he had received a letter through Father Barry from the sister who had left the convent, and added that he had written a letter in reply. The Thompsons, however, had refused to let him deliver it and he offered to go with him to the Thompsons' house. 'The Bishop repeated the circumstances which he had heard the sister had left the convent and I informed him that I personally could not see any sign of insanity about the girl, who, in fact, appeared to be perfectly sane.'

The Inspector, under cross-examination, is asked as to whether his relations with the Bishop have since been a little strained. 'We have not spoken since,' he says, adding that he did not think I was of unsound mind and he regarded the matter ended as far as the police were concerned.

Mr Campbell takes up cross-examination: 'Did you not hear officially that the government medical officer had said that she was insane?'

'Yes, on the 2nd August, some days after the interview with the Bishop.'

'Were you aware shortly after the 25th that she had been taken away secretly from Wagga?'

'I knew nothing about her movements until 2 August. I knew no more than the man in the moon. There were all sorts of rumours.'

'You were using the whole resources of the police and were unable to get any information?'

'Yes.'

'There was no trace of her at all?'

'Well, nobody who knew of it would tell me.'

'You continued your searches for the plaintiff till 4 August, and reported that you were unable to ascertain her whereabouts?'

'Yes.'

★★★

Doctor William Johnstone Binns, of Kogarah, is next to be called and, answering Mr Shand, says he has been practising for fourteen years. He went to Mrs Touchell's residence, in response to a telephone message, on 4 August, last year, at about 7 p.m.

'I examined Miss Partridge to see if I could find anything mentally wrong with her. I asked her questions about her family and if she could recall her journey to Australia, which she was able to answer. She was quietly dressed and perfectly self-possessed, a little restrained, and a little reserved. Miss Partridge told me she was on good terms with the inmates of the convent and had no reason to suppose they would be spiteful towards her. She said she did not desire to change her religious belief. She explained that the determination to leave the convent was arrived at suddenly, but she had been tired of the life for a couple of months before.'

'Take a girl like this, brought up in a convent; supposing if what she told you happened, would you think it an unreasonable thing that she should think she was being poisoned?'

'No, I think it would be the most natural deduction in the world for a person of her experience.'

Mr Campbell begins his cross-questioning by directing Doctor Binns' attention to the evidence given by the plaintiff relating to the fear she said she entertained that she was to be murdered on the occasion when she was given a dose of oil. He asks Doctor Binns whether this did not indicate a morbid delusion on her part.

'The impression I got was that the shock of the change in the attitude of the inmates produced in her mind the thought that she was going to be poisoned.'

'But,' Mr Campbell says, 'she had been on good terms with everybody at the convent before. Why should she entertain the fear that she was to be murdered?'

'It was only a natural deduction in the circumstances. In my opinion, the sudden change in the attitude of the other inmates awakened in her the fear that she was to be poisoned or injured in some way.'

'Would you go further and say that there was no evidence of insanity?'

'If there were other things, there would be evidence.'

'What other things?'

'Delusions or, if previous to that, she had been refusing food on the grounds that she believed it had been poisoned.' Doctor Binns went on to say that he had no reason to disbelieve what she said.

With his cross-examination over, there is a luncheon adjournment before the next witness is called. The queue outside has been forming since twelve o'clock and by degrees it has grown until another hundred or more people lined up for the afternoon session. At 1.45 p.m. their patience is rewarded and they are released in sections. In a few minutes, the gallery is again crowded.

Mr Boyce takes over from Mr Shand to question Mrs Jessie Burgess. I smile across at her as she begins her evidence. 'I live a short distance from Mount Erin Convent. At about 2 p.m. on Saturday, 24 July, one of my children told me there was a nun at the door. She looked as though she had been crying. She asked could she use the telephone and remained in our home for about three hours. I gave her a cup of tea. She was sitting in the dining room looking at photographs. I had very little conversation with her. So far as I could see there was nothing mentally wrong with her.'

'You saw her again in the evening?'

'Yes. A knock came on the back door and, on going out, I saw her again. She came inside and I gave her shoes and some clothes. At her suggestion we went away. We went to the Thompsons. There was nothing to indicate she was other than rational.'

Mr Campbell rises and asks, 'When she opened the door of the dining room she knew the nuns had come?'

'Yes.'

'She appeared to go away quite willingly?'

'Yes. She did not speak.'

'When Miss Partridge came to your place the second time what did she say?'

'I wanted her to stay and wanted to put her to bed, but she said, "I must get away from here. This will be the first house they will come to."'

Mr Campbell then asks, 'Did she say anything to you about the other sisters having given her medicine which made her sick?'

'No.'

'Did she not tell you they had tried to poison her?'

'No. Nothing like that.'

★★★

The next witness is called. Doctor Alexander Edward Gibbs states he had examined me in his official capacity of Second Government Medical Officer at the Reception House in August 1920. He had attended cases almost daily there for three years.

'Did you believe the plaintiff's statement that they had attempted to murder her?'

'I thought that she thought so.'

'Did you think it was a fact or a delusion?'

'In my opinion, it was not a delusion.'

'Then what was it?'

'An inference drawn from certain events that occurred. It may have been wrong, but it did not amount to a delusion.'

Mr Campbell begins, 'What conclusion did you come to when you examined her at the Reception House?'

'That she was perfectly sane.'

Mr Shand asks, 'Did Doctor Chisholm Ross agree with you?'

'Yes.'

★★★

Mrs Letitia Howell is called to the witness box and tells the court she lives near Adelong, she is the wife of a grazier in the district, and a sister of Mrs Thompson of Wagga.

In answer to Mr Boyce, Mrs Howell says that I arrived at her home, which is forty-two miles from Wagga, on a Sunday night, in July, accompanied by Mrs Thompson and three men.

'Miss Partridge remained with me for four days, the others leaving on the night of arrival. So far as I could see during that time, Miss Partridge appeared as sane as I am.' Mrs Howell went on to say that I wrote two letters to my brother, which she (the witness) had posted.

'Did you notice the plaintiff's hands after she came to your house?'

'Yes; they were very rough.'

'What did that indicate?'

'That she had been doing very rough work.'

99

Mr Campbell cross-questions her and asks, 'Is Mr Barton a friend of yours?'

'No.'

'Do you know anything of Mr Barton?'

'No, nothing at all.'

★★★

Court proceedings finish for the day. A considerable number of people are to be seen at the principal exits. But less than a dozen individuals witness our departure back through the gate we entered this morning.

Chapter Sixteen

On Wednesday, His Honour takes his seat and Mr Shand says he will close the case for the plaintiff.

Mr Campbell says that before Mr Shand did that he would like to ask me one or two further questions. I go back into the witness box.

'You said that on one occasion Sister Agatha thumped you? Did you complain to anyone about it?'

'No, I did not at that time.'

'You brought a dowry to the order?'

'No. If you are fully educated, they will take you without a dowry.'

'You knew, did you not, that the diocesan inspector had reported that you ought not to be continued in your teaching through lack of control over the pupils?'

'I did not. At Ganmain, the inspector was quite pleased with my teaching.'

Mr Shand rises. 'How long were you teaching altogether?'

'Five and a half years.'

'Had any complaint been made about the way you conducted the class or of the discipline during those five and a half years?'

'No complaints were made except at Wagga, where I had difficulty with a class of boys.'

Returning to my seat, I lean forward to hear what Mr Campbell is saying as he approaches the bench.

'The plaintiff has failed to make a legal case and legal action should be terminated.' Leading counsel for Bishop Dwyer argues for a non-suit. I understand nothing of the argument that follows, which is heavily fortified with an armoury of case law.

Finally, His Honour concludes, 'I think it is better I should take the opinion of the jury on questions of fact. I express no opinion myself at present. I am influenced very largely by this: if I am wrong in allowing the case to go to the jury, then it will be possible for the Court, in setting the matter right, to determine the matter finally, without putting the parties to the expense of a new trial. I refuse the non-suit.'

The gallery, occupied mostly by women, leaves the court, confused over the ceaseless flow of words after the Court Bailiff announces that proceedings will be resumed at ten o'clock tomorrow morning for the opening for the Defence.

Chapter Seventeen

The court bailiff calls the first witness for the defence. Wearing a heavy black overcoat in keeping with the cold, wintry day, confident strides take Bishop Joseph Wilfred Dwyer to the witness box to be sworn in.

Opening his case, Mr Campbell asks, 'What is the relation of the Bishop to the Community?'

'The Bishop has charge of everything in the diocese, including all religious orders,' he answers. 'I have nothing to do with the internal administration excepting parochial wants or to visit the community and to see that the establishment is being conducted according to its rules and regulations and see that the financial state of the institution is satisfactory. I also have to find out if any individual member has any complaint to make, either regarding her superiors, or her confreres. I have also to know about every member who enters the institution as a postulant, and have to ascertain if they are perfectly voluntarily being professed before they take vows.'

'These institutions perform a public or communal service?'

'Yes, a very great service. The service they perform for the inmates themselves is that they help them to aim at and, as far as is humanly possible, attain spiritual perfection if they observe their rules and regulations. That is one of the primary objects of the institutions. With regard to the people outside, they supply the wants of education and of charity, in the way of attending to the sick, poor and the destitute. This Presentation Order is an educational establishment.'

His portly presence in the witness box causes Mrs Touchell to mumble, 'What a pompous man!'

I am staring squarely into the Bishop's face and will soon learn why he laid down the law so recklessly and branded me insane.

'Have you any duty with regard to the members of the community who may desire to leave?' Mr Campbell asks.

'I have to investigate cases of complaints of unhappiness, if any, and see if they can be in any way remedied. If the appellant wishes to leave the community, I have to see that arrangements are made that she may go in a decent manner to parents, relatives, or friends.'

'Have you any duty with regard to seeing that provision is made for her needs, and passage to her people?'

'Yes, out of charity the sisters are obliged to see to her safe return to her people, and to supply her with reasonable expenses, or whatever she needs for the journey.'

'You knew the plaintiff before 24 July?'

'Yes; but I knew very little about her. I met her, I think, on three occasions to speak to, and on these occasions would not have seen her for more than two minutes.'

'One of these occasions was on the episcopal visit in May when you put questions to her, individually, so that the answers are perfectly free?'

'Yes.'

'Did she give you any indication of being dissatisfied?'

'None whatever.'

The letter I wrote to the Bishop at the dressing table in Mrs Thompson's bedroom is produced.

Sunday, 25 July 1920

Your Lordship
I, Sister M. Liguori, was not treated at Wagga Wagga Convent as I ought. I tried to do my duty the same as the rest of the sisters, but my health was broken down. I asked for medicine. The doctor gave me poison to end my life. I fled from the convent. I do not wish on any account to go back to Mount Erin. My deathbed was fixed for me at Mount Erin.

104

*I got into it (just like me). I drank the poison (just like me).
The hand of God sustained me.*

*I fled to the protection of a stranger who is giving me a
holiday and taking me in.*

*I will ask to return to another convent if I wish. I will
ask your permission to stay with friends otherwise. Are you
satisfied?*

*Yours sincerely
Sister M Liguori*

How many times had I read it over, ensuring every word was
perfect? Here it is now, held in evidence against me. Do they not
understand that I was forbidden by the vow of obedience to comment
on what was done to me and I always obeyed without question? I
had added the words 'just like me' in brackets before sealing it in
an envelope.

Mr Campbell breaks into my thoughts, asking the Bishop, 'Then
you wrote two letters?'

'Yes. I replied to Sister Liguori's letter and I also wrote to Mr
and Mrs Thompson.' Mr Campbell produces the Bishop's letter
to me.

Mr Shand objects that it had not been delivered, but Mr Campbell
contends that the letter would indicate the state of the Bishop's mind
if it goes to the question of malice. Mr Justice Ferguson agrees.

I listen carefully to what the Bishop wrote.

Tuesday, 27 July 1920

*I have just returned from Albury, and received the letter
you sent to me. I regret the course you have taken without
consulting me, and am willing to see you if you wish, and I
am writing to the people who have taken it upon themselves
to shelter you. I enclose a copy of the letter which I have sent
to Mr and Mrs Thompson.*

The letter the Bishop wrote to the Thompsons is read out.

Mr and Mrs Robert Thompson
Coleman Street
Wagga Wagga

Tuesday, 27 July 1920

Dear Sir and Madam
On my return from Albury last evening I was put into possession of full particulars of the departure of Sister M. Liguori and of her being cared for at your home. Whilst endorsing the thanks already expressed to you by the Reverend Mother for the accommodation extended by you to Sister Liguori, I feel duty bound to express the opinion that you have erred in two respects.

Firstly, in failing to at once disclose on Saturday evening to the Reverend Mother or the priest in charge at the Bishop's house or to the friends who were searching for the sister that she was with you, and thus saving all concerned a most anxious and distressing night. Instead of giving such information, I am advised that the sister's presence under your roof was denied. Secondly, in refusing Father Barry an interview with the sister on Sunday last, or to receive clothing sent to her by the convent authorities. I am also impelled from consideration for Sister Liguori herself and her people, for the sisters of Mount Erin, and for the Catholic community and myself, to call upon you personally to seek an interview with Sister Liguori in the presence of yourselves, if you so wish, one or two gentlemen I may bring with me, to ascertain from the sister personally why she came away from the convent, and what her complaints may be; what her condition of health is, and to invite her to return to the convent, to inform her she is most welcome to return if she so desires, and, knowing her act to have arisen from some temporary hallucination, to ensure her she is most readily forgiven by her superior and myself. Also that, if she insists on remaining away from the convent for some little time, there are several highly respectable Catholic families who have informed me they will be only too pleased to make her comfortable and at home. That if she will not return to conventual life then the convent authorities will provide her reasonable expenses for comforts and passage to her own people. May I also say that I deem it to be your duty to exercise every influence you may have to induce her to return to her duties, and dissuade her from taking any ill-advised action, which may be to her discredit. Should Sister Liguori refuse to return and persist in remaining on your hands, then you must recognize you are taking upon yourselves a very great responsibility, for which you alone must answer.

I remain
Yours truly
J W DWYER, Bishop of Wagga

The Bishop faces the jury, 'First, my duty was to try and take the place of the sisters who could not do what I was doing. They appealed to me, and I simply wanted to verify the state of this patient's condition. She had gone away from our keeping, and we did not know where she was. The police had failed to find her, and the only way left open to us was to get her examined by medical people, to find what her condition was. If she were to be declared sane by the authorities, my duty would cease, as far as her person is concerned. If she were declared to be insane, I would have to see that the convent provided her with treatment in hospital until she became well. If she wished to go back, she could go back. But, if she wished to leave, I would have to see that she was provided with the means to take her back to her own home again.'

The Bishop continues, 'By 29 July, the police had lost all trace of the missing sister and I sought advice from Mr James Sheekey, a local solicitor in Wagga. He suggested I take the matter to Sydney. I went to the Attorney General's office in the city who said there was nothing he could do as it was not a matter for his department, but a matter for the police and I was referred to the Inspector General of police, Mr James Mitchell, to whom I related the facts and showed him the letter Sister Liguori had written to me. Mr Mitchell thought the letter did not seem to be written by a person of normal mind and promised to contact the inspector at Wagga to ask him if he could locate the sister.'

The Bishop says he called again with Inspector Duprez on his arrival back at Wagga, asking him had he located Sister Liguori. The inspector replied, 'No.'

'Well, you'll have to arrest her,' I told him. To which he replied, 'I have nothing to arrest her for and I don't know where she is.'

The Bishop tells the court that he returned to Sydney on Tuesday, 3 August and saw Mr Mitchell, the Inspector General, again. He told him that nothing could be learned of the missing nun after an exhaustive search. Mr Mitchell made some telephone calls and the Bishop was driven to the central police court where he was introduced to the chamber magistrate, Mr Camphin, who listened to an account of the whole affair and said he thought he could issue a warrant based on the information he had. 'When I produced the letter Sister Liguori had written, Mr Camphin was convinced that she was mentally deranged.'

There is no sign of remorse on his face, nor hint of sorrow in his voice, when he states, 'On 3 August, I swore that I deemed Sister Liguori to be of unsound mind and without visible means of support.'

'I must ask you whether you believed the statements on the information about her being deemed to be of unsound mind and not having sufficient means of support?'

'Yes, I believed those statements.'

'Did you have any other desire or purpose in the action that you took than for the plaintiff's protection and well-being?'

'None whatever.'

'You yourself have no power to give dispensation of vows, but you are the channel of application for that purpose?'

'Yes.'

'You received this application for dispensation?'

'Yes. I could not deal with it, but sent it on to the apostolic delegate. He dealt with it, and reported to me. The plaintiff was granted dispensation.'

'You received a letter from the plaintiff, written at Darlinghurst, on 12 August, in which she says, "Why not visit me here when it is all over?"'

'Yes.'

'Did you know when she left the Reception House?'

'I heard she left on 13 August.'

'Were you always willing to see her?'

'Yes, always and never able to.'

★★★

Mr Shand is immediately on his feet for cross-examination. 'You took no part in the proceedings at the Lunacy Court when she was brought before the magistrate?'

'Not on the first day. On the second day I was represented by my solicitor.'

'Did you tender any evidence?'

'None whatever.'

'Have you told us everything that took place between you and the magistrate at Sydney?'

'I think so. I did not conceal anything from him.'

'I am not asking if you concealed anything. Is that all you told him?'

'I believe so.'

'Did you tell the chamber magistrate that you believed she was in the hands of extremists?'

'I believe so.'

'And you wanted to get her out of their hands?'

'I did not say it in that way.'

'Did you not say you wanted to get the woman out of the hands of "these extremists"?'

'Yes, for the purpose of being examined.'

'You believed she was in the hands of extremists?'

'She was out of my hands.'

'Did you mean ultra-Protestants when you said extremists?'

'No.'

'When you swear that when you used the word "extremists" you did not mean men of the Orange Lodge?'

'And that sort, yes.'

'Did you know that Doctor Leahy had asked for a warrant at Wagga and that his application had been refused?'

'I did not.'

'Didn't Mr Sheekey *(solicitor)* tell you that he had applied for a warrant, and that it had been refused on the grounds that there was no evidence that Sister Liguori was not without lawful means of support?'

'No; on the grounds that the magistrate wanted to visit the patient and see for himself what she was like.'

'Did he tell you that the magistrate said she was supposed to be at Thompson's, and that, as Mr Thompson was a man of substance, she could not be said to be without means of support?'

'I don't remember that.'

'Will you deny that it was said?'

'He told me that the magistrate wanted to visit the patient, and that she had gone from Thompson's. He wanted to see for himself what the sister was like.'

'Why did you not tell the magistrate in Sydney that the warrant had been refused?'

'He did not ask me.'

'And you did not think it important enough to mention?'

'No.'

'Did you not instruct Leahy to issue a warrant before you left Wagga?'

'I asked him by telephone message whether he was prepared to back up his opinion by a certificate.'

'Did you suggest he should take out proceedings for the sister's arrest?'

'No; that was somebody else; I asked him for a certificate.'

There is a lunch break. When we step out into the corridor to wait for the Reverand Touchell, Mrs Touchell tugs at my sleeve. I stand still. Bishop Dwyer walks slowly past us. He is so deep in conversation with Mr Campbell that he doesn't see me.

★★★

M r Shand continues his cross-examination after lunch. 'When you came back from Albury on Monday evening, did you go to the convent?'

'Not that evening.'

'Would you not consider it an important matter that Doctor Leahy had never suggested Sister Liguori was insane up to that time?'

The Bishop says he might not have found any reason to suggest it up to that time.

'Were you told that Inspector Duprez had asked the Reverend Mother whether she had ever noticed any signs of insanity?'

'No; I don't remember being told that.'

'And the Reverend Mother had answered "No"?'

'I don't remember it.'

'You formed whatever opinion you might have formed with regard to this girl's condition from that letter, and the way she left the convent?'

'Yes.'

'Nothing else?'

'Only what I heard from Father Barry about the circumstances of her leaving, and the letter and the doctor's opinion, of course.'

'Did the doctor ever suggest to you prior to your swearing this information that there was anything except this letter and the fact that the plaintiff had left the convent to bring him to the conclusion that she was suffering from insanity?'

'He never suggested to me anything like that.'

'You didn't ask him whether he had noticed any sign of insanity before she left the convent?'

'No.'

'Did you deem her insane on July 27?'

'I do not think I have said I deemed her insane.'

'Did you regard her on July 27 as a person who could exercise sound judgment?'

'No. I did not.'

'Referring to the letter you wrote to Mrs Thompson before swearing the information in Sydney, you treated the girl as a perfectly free agent, who was capable of determining her own actions. Yet you suggested that Mrs Thompson should use her influence to induce this girl, whom you thought mentally deranged, to return to her duties?'

'Yes; to return to what she ought to do.'

'What did you mean by "action which may be to her discredit"?'

'By going away and not leaving the convent in the proper way.'

'You found out that Doctor Tivey had examined her. There was no animus between you and him?'

'None whatever.'

'Why did you not investigate the grounds of his belief?'

'First of all, he only had about ten minutes or a quarter of an hour in which to examine her, and that could not let a medical man form any opinion one way or another. Secondly, Doctor Leahy, who had known her for months, or perhaps years, had said he thought she was mentally deranged.'

'Do you tell me that you knew no more than that Doctor Leahy's opinion was formed from the circumstances of her leaving the convent and the letter of hers?'

'Yes.'

'Do I understand from you that you came to the conclusion as to the value of Doctor Leahy's opinion from the fact of him having seen her before?'

'He knew her history.'

'You never inquired whether Doctor Leahy had suspected insanity before?'

'No.'

'Why did you not apply to the local police magistrate for the warrant?'

'I had applied to the local police first. I was informed by Mr Sheekey that the local court refused it, the magistrate declining to take the responsibility on himself without seeing the patient.'

Chapter Eighteen

Mother Stanislaus makes her way noiselessly to the witness box. Only the rustle of her habit can be heard. Her sombre figure is a striking contrast to the strange motley gathered within the courtroom. She is more stooped than I remember. For over thirty years she has worked tirelessly, witnessing with pride the growth of Mount Erin Convent.

I had spent almost twelve years with her and we never spoke of home and Kildare. It was our commitment to God – to abandon the outside world and live totally for Him. I often wondered what she knew of my family that could have provided me with the tiniest scrap of solace. I had pleaded with her on the morning I left to be relieved of the arduous duties of a lay nun allowing me to return to my teaching post. That was the day I was finally crushed beneath a regime that demanded nothing less than total humility and obedience.

In a low voice, in half-light, Mother Stanislaus tells the court that her baptismal name is Mary Dunne. She has been connected with the community for forty-seven years and the role of Mother Superior is subject to election by the community. The election is held every three years, and one cannot hold office for more than two terms consecutively. She is the head of the order in New South Wales, and has seventy-eight nuns in her charge. At Mount Erin Convent, Wagga, there are about ninety resident boarders and between three and four hundred day pupils.

Mr Campbell rises to begin. 'Would it be correct to say that the duties of the plaintiff in the refectory were very arduous and very laborious?'

'It would not.' Mother Stanislaus says, 'The duties of the plaintiff in the refectory consisted of laying the table, but without any duties as to attendance, this being taken in weekly turns by sisters. After meals, the plaintiff helped to clear away and, with another sister, washed up small things, but each sister washed up her own knife and fork and spoon and put them away. Greasy plates were sent to the maids in the kitchen.'

I remember otherwise.

Mother Stanislaus says that for a short while after coming to the convent in 1918, another Reverend Mother who was in office had employed me to teach in the infant department of the primary school for an hour or an hour and a half a day, but then my duties were changed.

'The plaintiff was of a very nervous temperament and she complained greatly of headaches and sleeplessness.'

'Coming to 24 July,' Mr Campbell asks, 'had your attention been specially called to the plaintiff some days before?'

'Yes; I had been away for three weeks and returned three days before this occurrence. During that time Sister Liguori came to me in a very excited state. She was unhinged.'

'What did she tell you about her condition?'

'On the morning of the 24th she complained of a headache. She spoke in a way which made me realize she was not herself.'

'What did you observe about her on that fateful Saturday?'

'I observed that she was flushed; she was excited and different.'

'You knew she had left the convent that afternoon?'

'Yes, at about two o'clock.'

'And the first you knew of it was when you got a message from Father Barry?'

'Yes.'

'And, under your instructions, two of the sisters were sent after her and that Sister Liguori had come back with them?'

'Yes. She came straight to my office.'

'What did you or she say?'

'I looked very sad at her, and she came across to me, and said, "Mother, I am sorry." I said, "Now go and change your clothing."

She was wet, because it had been raining heavily, and she then went away.'

'Is there any suggestion that you scolded her or reprimanded her in any way?'

'No, not in any way – not a single word.'

'What happened next?'

'Sister Brendan got her a cup of tea, and she had some toast and an egg. In the meantime, I had rung up for Doctor Leahy.'

'The next time you saw Sister Liguori she was in the presence of Doctor Leahy, was she not?'

'Yes.'

'Do you remember asking her whether anybody in the convent had done anything to make her go away?'

'Yes, and she said, "You were all very kind to me."'

Replying to Mr Campbell, the witness says that the plaintiff had told her that someone had blamed her wrongly for taking a broom, and asked her where it was. The Reverend Mother had said there was not any harm in that, and the plaintiff replied, 'No, but it worried me.' The plaintiff also said that a sister worried her by asking at what time the dinner was to be.

'Did you speak unkindly to her?'

'Not one word. I never found any fault with her.'

'Doctor Leahy was there all the time?'

'Yes.'

'The doctor told her she needed rest, and advised her that she should go to bed.'

'Is there any difficulty in a sister leaving if she is dissatisfied with life in the order, or her position?' Mr Campbell continued.

'There is no difficulty. If she makes her wishes known it would be communicated to the Bishop, and he would do everything necessary in the matter. The plaintiff was acquainted with the canon law.'

'You were aware, of course, of the charges which the plaintiff made against you, and the doctor, in that letter which she wrote. I think you have seen that letter, have you not?'

'Yes; I have seen it.'

'Is there the slightest ground for her charge that you and the sister and the doctor had determined to murder her, and in pursuance of that intention had caused to be administered to her a dose of poison?'

'I have not the smallest notion of such a thing.'

'Do you know how oil is ordinarily administered in the convent?'

'It is generally given in coffee, black coffee.'

'Had you anything to do with the administering of the oil that night?'

'No, nothing whatever. I knew it was to be given, but I knew nothing about it afterwards.'

'In the whole course of your connection with the convent, have you ever known unkindness to be practised towards any sister?'

'No, never.'

'You remember Inspector Duprez and Doctor Tivey and some other people coming to the convent on the Sunday morning?'

'Yes.'

'Can you give the Court your recollection of what took place between yourself, Inspector Duprez and Doctor Tivey?'

'Mr Duprez asked me about the sister's friends. When I asked him whether she was sane, he told me Doctor Tivey had said she was quite sane, and I said I did not know how she could be quite sane when she left the convent as she did. I said that Doctor Leahy had treated her for headaches, etc, and knew she was not altogether normal. Mr Duprez asked me whether I could not leave her with the Thompsons and I said I could not do that, as I was responsible for her to her parents, and I wished very much to get her back. Mr Duprez said it had been stated that she did not want to go back, and I said we did not wish to keep her, but wanted to provide for her. Mr Duprez said Doctor Tivey had told him Mrs Tivey could not get a maid for love or money, and they would be glad to have her. I said I could not allow that, and I was very positive about the matter.'

'Was there any reference to her parents then?'

'I was asked whether her father and mother were living, and I said yes. I also said she had three sisters, and one brother, and that the brother was in Hong Kong.'

'Was any reference made to your intentions if she returned?'

'Yes; I said we would send her to her parents, and it was our wish to provide for her. I said that in the circumstances we could not keep her if she did not wish to stay, but we would provide for her.'

Mr Shand begins his cross-examination.

'What was troubling you very much was that she was in the hands of the Thompsons?'

'I would have been troubled if she had been in anybody's hands.'

'You took the view that if she left properly she was free to do so but, if she did not leave with permission, you had a right to get her back, and send her to her parents?'

'Yes.'

'You thought you were justified in getting her back to restore her to her parents?'

'Yes.'

'I put it this way: did the Bishop not say you were justified by hook or by crook in getting her back?'

'No, no.'

'Girls had left before and been brought back?'

'Yes.'

'Did another girl want to leave the convent and go and throw herself in the dam?'

'Yes. It was a case of temporary insanity.'

'She wanted to leave?'

'I don't think she knew what she wanted.'

'Did she ask to leave?'

'No, she did not.'

'And the first information you had of her intention to leave was finding her in the dam?'

'She did not inform anyone she wanted to leave.'

'Is there much of this insanity there?'

'No.'

'Do you keep medicines – drugs – at the convent?'

'Yes, medicine.'

'Have you a medicine called paraldehyde there?'

'I never heard of it, and think I am safe in saying no. We have just a few simple medicines.'

Mrs Touchell had told me that paraldehyde is a clear liquid and can easily be disguised in a cup of coffee. It is used to induce sleep in patients in a highly anxious state. A cold shiver runs through me, as I lay defenceless, fearing the punishment for my 'unpardonable crime'.

'About three weeks before 24 July Doctor Leahy had seen Sister Liguori?'

'Yes, she had influenza, I think.'

'There was nothing to suggest anything wrong with her mind then?'

'Not in connection with the influenza.'

Replying to further questions, the witness said she had been told, at the interview with Doctor Tivey, the inspector, and the constable, that the sister said she did not want to go back to the convent. 'I do not remember telling Doctor Tivey that I saw no signs of insanity about the sister prior to leaving. I do not think I could have said that.'

'Immediately after the occurrence, you wrote to the Thompsons. Did you suggest there was anything wrong with her mind?'

'I wrote to thank them for taking care of her that night.'

'Of course, if you looked upon her as being deranged, you would not feel grieved at what she did?'

'I did feel grieved. The reason I wrote to the Thompsons was that on the night before we suffered intense anxiety, not knowing what had become of this poor child, not knowing whether she was dead. When we heard she was at the Thompsons we were relieved, and were thankful to them for giving her the hospitality of their house.'

'And you sent her clothing?'

'I didn't send her habit, but I sent warm clothing, as we knew she had none.'

'Anticipating she would remain at the Thompsons'?'

'I did not know. I was waiting for the Bishop to return from Albury. I did not know what to think.'

'But you contemplated she was going to remain at the Thompsons when you wrote saying you were sending her some clothes, and that anything else she required would be supplied?'

'I suppose I did.'

Mr Shand reads the following letter, written by the witness:

25 July

Dear Mr and Mrs Thompson – just a line to say I am grateful to hear that our dear sister had the shelter of your home last night. We have been very grieved over her actions. I am sending over a few articles of clothing, and anything she needs will be supplied.

With best wishes, dear Mr and Mrs Thompson.

Mr Shand asks, 'You regard leaving the convent as a very serious breach?'

'Yes.'

'One of the most serious one of the order could commit?'

'Yes, if responsible for her actions.'

'It would not be looked upon in a friendly way by those who surrounded her?'

'No.'

'Did you find the plaintiff a truthful girl?'

'Yes.'

'And when she came back from Burgess's she said she had been accused of lying?'

'She never used that word. She said she had been charged with taking a broom and was worried over it.'

'When did you first notice her flushed?'

'On the Thursday and Friday preceding and the Saturday that she went away.'

'Did you relieve her of her duties at all?'

'No; her duties were light.'

★★★

Mr Campbell rises to re-examine Mother Stanislaus.

'On the Saturday that the plaintiff disappeared from the convent the second time did you ring up Doctor Leahy?'

'Yes, I rang him up on the Saturday night.'

'Did he join in the search party?'

'Yes, I believe he did.'

'Would it be correct to say that the plaintiff was asked to do in ten minutes what it would take half an hour to do?'

'Oh, no, she had the whole day to perform the duties she had.'

Chapter Nineteen

Sister Mary Brendan is called next. Her short, squat figure struts to the witness box and tells the court her baptismal name is Annie Dunne. She is a professed member of the community of Presentation nuns at Wagga, and has been connected with it for sixteen years. She had never known a sister member of the community to be subjected to any unkindness or to be dealt with oppressively.

'I have known Sister Liguori for eleven and a half years, and went through the whole of my novitiate with her. I was at the Wagga house with her for two and a half years before 24 July. We came there at about the same time. During that period I did not see the slightest unkindness practised on the part of the community towards Sister Liguori. I was Sister Liguori's constant companion, and was always on good terms with her, terms of affection. I remember Sister Liguori on the afternoon of the 24th. I met her coming back from the Burgesses', and I told her she looked ghastly. After an interview with the Reverend Mother, I took her to the refectory where she had some tea and toast. I accompanied her upstairs and, as her clothing was very wet and muddy, I helped her to change, and got her some warm water for a wash. Sister Liguori expressed a wish to change her headdress for Mass the next morning. She seemed in a very agitated state of mind, but she became more composed before she went down to see the doctor.'

Sister Brendan went on to say she helped prepare my bed for me.

'When I prepared her medicine, she asked if it was the doctor's orders, and I said, "Yes." I prepared the oil myself in black coffee. The coffee was no stronger than usual. I assisted her to sit up, putting my arms around her while she was taking it. Sister Liguori took a biscuit. I then made her comfortable lying down. She did not complain about the dose, and did not suggest that there was anything unusual in the flavour.'

Sister Brendan said she sat with me for about twenty minutes, during which time I was perfectly quiet.

'Thinking that Sister Liguori would get some sleep, I sprinkled her with holy water, as was the custom. I then retired to another part of the room. While there, I heard her move. She expressed a wish for a cup of cocoa. I told her it was rather soon after the medicine, but said I would give it to her later. She was tossing about a good deal. At half past seven, I was sent for by the Mother Superior, and sought permission from her to remain with the sister. When I returned the sister was not in bed. I went to the bathroom and found she was in the lavatory. I told her she was sure to get a cold. I offered to get her a hot water bottle from downstairs, as her feet were very cold. She assured me she would be in bed when I returned.

'But when I returned, she was not there. I did not see her again at the convent. There was nothing unusual about sprinkling holy water on the bed. I did not say to the plaintiff at any time that she might die of pneumonia or that, after administering the oil, "You won't want another dose." I did not take her pillows from her and lay her flat on the bed and put her hands down the side, nor did I say, "You won't get out of bed for six months."'

'Is it a fact that while she was lying in bed you were peeping around the curtains at her?'

'The curtains were not drawn.' Sister Brendan proceeded to say that the use of holy water about the sleeping chamber was observed in every Catholic home.

'I am talking about the cells.'

'Yes. It was sprinkled every night.'

'Were you and the plaintiff together taught that the sprinkling of holy water was in any way associated with the idea of death?'

'No.'

Cross-examined by Mr Shand, Sister Brendan said she was not related to the Reverend Mother.

'I suppose you regard this leaving the convent without permission as a very serious matter?'

'It is a matter of the conscience of the person herself.'

'Is it not laid down that it is a serious matter?'

'Yes, it is very serious.'

'Did you look at her going to the Burgesses', without permission, as rather a disgrace?'

'It depends how she looked at it.'

'By leaving in the way she did, you would regard her as having disgraced, not only herself, but the community, by her action?'

'Yes.'

'Would you regard a girl who had disgraced the community as deserving of a little fright, if not punishment?'

'Not punishment.'

'Didn't you think a little fright would do her good?'

'Not in her frame of mind.'

'With regard to the sprinkling of holy water, don't the nuns usually sprinkle their own room?'

'They always sprinkle their own room at night.'

'Do you know any other occasion in the two and a half years, when any nun sprinkled holy water at night except the sister herself?'

'Yes. I have known several occasions when sisters sprinkled holy water around the room.'

Mr Shand's questioning becomes more brisk. 'Tell me any time before.'

'I can't give you the exact time. Every night on retiring the sister who puts out the lights sprinkles holy water.'

'I thought you said the nun did it herself?'

'She could do it.'

'I am asking you as a matter of fact, did not the nuns do it themselves?'

'Yes.'

'Did you have any conversation with the plaintiff when she came in at teatime?'

'I asked her what she was going to do and she said she would like to go to bed.'

'You didn't ask what had happened to her, why she had gone away, or sympathise with her?'

'I showed sympathy towards her.'

'You said you were with her for half an hour, yet you did not speak to her more than you have told us?'

'I spoke on various matters but cannot really recall what was said.'

'I take it that whatever she said was sensible?'

'No, she was looking very agitated.'

'Will you tell the jury anything she said that was not sensible?'

'She complained of her head very much.'

'I want to know anything else she said?'

'I cannot recall anything.'

'When you gave her the oil did you say anything to her?'

'No.'

'You just handed it to her and said, "Here's the oil"?'

'I just gave it to her with a biscuit.'

'Then from the time she took that dose till you left her did you speak?'

'She was just lying comfortable and I did not speak to her. I thought she was going to sleep.'

'What became of the utensil which contained the oil?'

'It was a small teacup and I took it downstairs that night.'

'What were your duties?'

'My duties were at the boarding school, but another sister had taken my place.'

'Did you hear the plaintiff vomiting?'

'No.'

'It was a cold night?'

'Yes, a very cold night.'

'When did you first hear that the sister had said that you had given her a dose, alleged to be oil, that she had taken it, and that you had told her she would not want another dose?'

'When I read it in the papers.'

'If you gave her the oil and said, "You won't want another dose," that would be a very wrong thing to say?'

'Yes, it would, in her frame of mind.'

'Supposing in her state of mind you suggested that she would not want another dose, what would that convey to you, do you think?'

Sister Brendan, lowering her head, does not answer.

Chapter Twenty

Mother Mary Clare tells Mr Campbell that her baptismal name is Mary Herbert. She had been mother of novices at Mount Erin convent but now held the office of bursar.

'We have heard that you were very hard as mother of the novices.'

'I tried to fit them to be decent members of the community.'

Mother Clare said she went to Mrs Burgess's house on 24 July with another nun, and Sister Liguori returned quite voluntarily with them. She was not spoken to harshly, but was given a cup of tea and put to bed.

'Did you talk with her on her return to the convent?'

'Yes. She said there had been a disturbance about a broom, and that someone had asked her when dinner would be ready.'

'Did you ask her how she was when you went to the Burgesses'?'

'I said to her, "Reverend Mother is very anxious to see you." She then said, "I will go back," and returned at once.'

On cross-examination, Mother Clare tells Mr Shand that on the previous Thursday she had noticed that Sister Liguori, instead of being rather slow in her movements, was moving quickly about, and had become very talkative. Up to the time she left, she went about her ordinary duties.

Mother Clare was unable to remember the details of a conversation between Doctor Tivey, Inspector Duprez and the Reverend Mother on the Sunday morning. She did not hear Doctor Tivey asking the Reverend Mother whether Doctor Leahy had ever suggested there was anything wrong with Sister Liguori mentally. She could, however, recollect Doctor Tivey saying that his examination showed her to be normal. When Inspector Duprez remarked that he thought Sister Liguori could leave if she wanted to, Mother Clare said, "Yes, but there was no necessity for her to go in the way she did, as she could have left, as any of us can, by asking permission."

'Do you remember Inspector Duprez saying that Sister Liguori did not want to return to the convent?'

'I think he did say something like that.'

'Do you remember the Reverend Mother being asked whether she had noticed anything strange about the girl before she left the convent?'

'I do not remember.'

Mr Campbell rises from his seat. 'Are you prepared to say whether the plaintiff's duties at the convent were heavy or difficult?'

'No, not heavy.'

Chapter Twenty-one

M r Flannery, KC (for the defence) calls Doctor William Leahy who tells the court that he has been practising at Wagga for about twenty-five years and is Government Medical Officer there. Questioned about my health, he said he had known me since 1915, and thought I was neurasthenic, that I was of a highly nervous temperament and suffered a good deal from insomnia, gastrointestinal weakness – weakness of digestion and constipation. He went on to say my circulation was feeble, that I had clammy hands, my pulse was weak and I was of a neurotic temperament. He did not think my physical condition was very strong and that I became easily exhausted by small efforts.

'Before 24 July, when did you last see her and prescribe for her?'

'About 13 June.'

'For what general disorder did you prescribe?'

'For insomnia and nervousness.'

'And headaches?'

'Yes.'

Questioned about 24 July, Doctor Leahy relates how he felt my pulse and examined me. He found I was a bit excited, that I looked very pale and he did not put any questions to me because he did not want to disturb me owing to the condition I was in. He prescribed for my condition.

'Is this the prescription?' (produced)

'Yes.'

Mr Shand stands up. 'Is this the original document?'

'No, it is only a copy.'

Mr Shand objects. 'Where is the original?'

'It was sent to the local chemist.'

Mr Flannery continues: 'Did you prescribe paraldehyde for her?'

'No.'

'What did you think her condition required?'

'I thought she was mentally unhinged and needed medical treatment.'

Doctor Leahy said his interview with me lasted about a quarter of an hour. He then left the convent but returned about nine o'clock when he got a telephone message from the Reverend Mother.

'Did you see a letter which the sister wrote to the Bishop in which she made certain charges?'

'Yes.'

'Did you form a certain opinion from that letter as to the sister's mental condition?'

'Well, it confirmed my previous opinion that the person who produced that letter was suffering from delusions of persecution, and that she was of unsound mind at the time she wrote the letter.'

'When did you first express an opinion to the defendant?'

'On 28th July. Bishop Dwyer rang me up and said: "I believe you have expressed the opinion that Sister Liguori was of unsound mind?" I said, "Yes." He asked if I would give a certificate to that effect, and I said, "Yes."'

'On that date, what did you know of the plaintiff's whereabouts?'

'I believed she was at the Thompsons and was in hiding.'

'Did that affect your conclusion?'

'As she was concealing herself from her friends I came to the conclusion she was still of unsound mind.'

'Is it possible for symptoms of unsound mind in a person to be apparent one day and not on a subsequent day?'

'Yes.'

★★★

Mr Shand springs to his feet to begin his cross-examination. 'And I suppose you will admit the converse is true – that a person may be subject to a temporary attack which passes off?'

'Yes, that is true.'

'And, as far as you know, this girl who had a delusion on 24 July may have been perfectly right on 25, 26 or 27 July?'

'Yes.'

'I think you will agree that a case of one delusion is remarkable in lunacy?'

'Well, there are different kinds, really.'

'Will you admit that the existence of only one delusion is a very uncommon thing?'

'No. She may have one delusion resulting from a fear that perhaps she was to be violently dealt with.'

'What do you believe constitutes a delusion?'

'A wrong belief that remains for a certain time and affects the judgment of the person.'

'Do you keep records of the cases you attend?'

'I have no records of my attendance at the convent.'

'Did you keep any record of the symptoms of this girl?'

'No.'

Doctor Leahy says that in April he prescribed for a nasal douche. He said I suffered from catarrh and he had also prescribed for indigestion and constipation and headache. He said I dwelt a great deal on my symptoms, and said I was suffering from sleeplessness, and had dyspepsia.

Mr Shand refers to the affidavit drawn up in the offices of Mr James Clements Sheekey, a solicitor practising at Wagga. (The document is produced.)

★★★

On the first day of August 1920, William Leahy, medical practitioner in Wagga Wagga, in the State of New South Wales, made the following oath before J K O'Kelly, JP.

1. *I am a duly qualified medical practitioner, residing at Wagga Wagga, in the State aforesaid.*
2. *I know and am well acquainted with Brigid Partridge, a*

member of the religious order of the Presentation nuns residing at Wagga Wagga, and known in religion as Sister Liguori.

3. *I have been attending the said Sister Mary Liguori for the past five years.*

4. *I am of the opinion that she is of unsound mind, and that she should be placed under proper care and control.*

5. *I am informed, and verily believe the same to be true, that she is at present in a certain private dwelling house in Wagga Wagga aforesaid, and if such is the case I am of the opinion that she should not receive the proper care and control that her mental condition requires. Further, I am of the opinion that she should be placed in a hospital for the insane for treatment and observation.*

6. *I am informed, and verily believe the same to be true, that the said Sister Mary Liguori is without sufficient means of support.*

7. *I am the Government Medical Officer stationed at Wagga Wagga aforesaid.*

(Signed) W. LEAHY
Sworn by the Department on the first day of August 1920 at Wagga Wagga, before me,

(Signed) J K O'KELLY, JP

Mr Shand goes on to question the doctor about attending the chamber magistrate's office in Wagga with Mr Sheekey, a local solicitor. 'Did Mr Sheekey ask Mr Hazell, the chamber magistrate, for a warrant to be issued for the apprehension of this girl?'

'Yes.'

'Didn't Mr Hazell say, "Doctor Tivey has said she is sane. I am not satisfied of her insanity," and he refused to issue a warrant.'

'I don't remember it.'

Doctor Leahy is questioned with regard to the alterations he made to the affidavit: 'Want of means of support and Government Medical Officer.' Doctor Leahy says he knew that when I left the convent I had no money. He had added Government Medical Officer to confirm his correct title.

'But you believed that she was with people who were looking after her? Do you not swear that you believe she was with the Thompsons?'

'Am I to assume that they would support her?'

'You would not do that?'

'No.'

'Would you say she was or was not of a type subject to delusions?'

'Well, she was very nervous. I would say she would be subject to delusions.'

'What was there to base any delusion of fear in your mind before you saw the letter?'

'The fact of her running away for the smallest trifles.'

'Did that indicate fear?'

'Fear of what? In a person suffering from delusions it is very hard to follow the eccentricities of the mind.'

'When the plaintiff fled you knew her medical history?'

'Yes.'

'So far as subjection to delusion is concerned is chronic constipation an important symptom?'

The court leans forward to hear the doctor's answer. 'Yes.'

A look of bewilderment spreads over Mr Shand's face and he takes a moment before asking his next question.

'Have you ever had occasion before this to lay information against a person for being "deemed to be of unsound mind"?'

'Never.'

Mr Flannery rises. 'If you heard that on the night of the 24th her mind had mistaken black coffee and oil for a mixture that was not merely nauseous, but was different to the taste of coffee and oil, and smelt offensively, and that the offensive smell continued with her until the next day, what would you have considered that belief in her mind?'

'I did give weight to that when I saw her letter to the Bishop, and I came to the conclusion that amongst her other delusions she had a delusion of taste and smell.'

Mr Shand says, 'But she had been having tea and eating an egg; would not her delusions extend to that also?'

'But that was nutriment, not medicine, and would have different associations.'

Chapter Twenty-two

The proceedings on Monday, 11 July, mark the beginning of the end of the *Liguori Case* with no diminution of public interest on the eighth day of the trial. The queues outside the court are even larger than those of Friday.

Sergeant Mills, back on duty after a few days' leave, offers his usual broad smile when I arrive with Mrs Touchell. 'My colleagues have been telling me they have never seen so many people having urgent business to transact with lawyers and others inside the building. But their urgent business has to wait,' he laughs. 'The police are birds too full-fledged to be caught with chaff.'

'We'll miss you when this is all over, Sergeant Mills,' I tell him before entering the courtroom.

Sitting on the bench behind Counsel, I see Bishop Dwyer arriving at the same time as the barristers. Immediately Mr Justice Ferguson takes his seat, the jury makes another application for increased fees, and His Honour says he will consider the request.

★★★

James Clements Sheekey is called and his small frame barely reaches above the witness box. He states that he is a solicitor practising in Wagga. In reply to a question from Mr Flannery, he says the Bishop was not a client of his but he went to see him on 31 July in response to a telephone communication from him. He took with him an affidavit drawn up the previous day by Doctor Leahy.

'What did you tell the Bishop in respect to the chamber magistrate in Wagga?'

'I told him that Hazell appeared unwilling to act in the matter, and did not want to get mixed up with it. I discussed generally with the defendant the provisions of the Lunacy Act, in particular Section 5, which Doctor Leahy's affidavit covered. It was in respect to that section I had attended Hazell's office.'

'Did you give him advice?'

'I advised the Bishop to bring the matter to Sydney.'

Mr Shand rises to cross-examine the witness.

'Have you not taken a deep interest in this case, both as a churchman and as a professional man?'

'Not as a churchman, but as a professional man.'

'Your only interest has been a professional interest?'

'Yes.'

'But the matter excited a good deal of interest in Wagga, did it not?'

'It may have in some quarters.'

'Was it not a matter of general and topical conversation?'

'I cannot say whether it was a matter of topical conversation.'

'Was not the case reported in the newspapers at Wagga with big headings?'

'In one newspaper it was.'

'I suppose you read it?'

'Yes.'

'And yet your only interest in it was professional?'

'Yes.'

'You were in the office of the clerk of petty sessions on the 29th July, were you not?'

'I was there to get an affidavit sworn, that is all.'

'Did you say we want a warrant under Section 4 of the Lunacy Act for Sister Liguori, who has left the convent?'

'No. It was for the purpose of taking steps under Section 5 of the Lunacy Act. I told Hazell I was not concerned with Section 4, but with Section 5.'

The witness said that the first affidavit drawn up applied to Section 5 only and that he was responsible for the insertion of the paragraph relating to Doctor Leahy's opinion and belief as to the sufficiency of her support.

'Did Mr Hazell tell you that he was not satisfied that she was insane?'

'No.'

'Did he say this? "If the doctor is prepared to complain to me on oath that this person is deemed to be insane, and is not under proper care and control, I will take the necessary action to investigate it under Section 5."'

'No. Hazell said he would not act unless his personal safety was guaranteed.'

'Did he tell you what he meant by that?'

'Yes, he was frightened that the Thompsons might attack him, and do him some personal injury.'

The court breaks into laughter.

'Apparently they are desperate people?'

'I do not know them.'

The witness says that where an order is issued, it is communicated to the police of the whole state, and that if an information is sworn in Wagga the official course would be that a copy of the warrant would be sent to every police station.

'And do you suggest that where warrants are executed in that way the police who receive them do not exercise their best efforts to execute them?'

'I don't suggest anything of the kind.'

'Well, why would an information sworn in Sydney be more efficacious in stirring up the police than an information sworn in Wagga, and communicated to the police all over the state?'

The witness says a matter going from headquarters would always receive better attention. The local police had honestly tried to locate the woman, and had reported that they had failed to do so.

His Honour explains to the jury the difference between the two sections referred to, saying that Section 4 was the section which was acted upon in this case. That provided that, upon information on oath before a justice, a person deemed to be insane was without sufficient means of support, then the justice might make an order for the apprehension of that person in order that he or she might be brought before the court. Section 5 provided that when any person who, on oath, informed the justice that a person deemed to be insane was not under proper care and control, then the justice should either himself visit and examine such person and make inquiries into the case, or direct and authorize some medical practitioner to visit her and make inquiry and report, in writing, to a justice, and then the justice would act upon that report.

★★★

Bishop Dwyer, the defendant, is recalled.

Mr Shand refers to an article in the *Wagga Advertiser*. 'At a public concert in the Strand Theatre on March 16 did you say this?

> *"And now because Irishmen ask that they be given what the soldiers fought for, and are prepared to show their resentment of any interference, an army of murderers — the mongrel scum of England in the shape of the 'Black and Tans' — are devastating and robbing the country, and are telling the people that they are only rebels, and that they should be shot."'*

'I said something like that.'
'Did you say this?

> *"The Irish people want to live in peace as well as those of foreign lands. But they are asked to bow to the ruling of England, and be loyal to the British Empire. Although I try to be loyal to it because I have to, I cannot be loyal to the headquarters of it, because they have perpetrated cruelties on the Irish peasants."'*

'I think I did say it.'
He goes on to remark that he has nothing to do with England. He

is an Australian. He is loyal to the laws of Australia and he recognizes the King of England as the King of Australia.

The court sits up to listen to the Bishop airing his views on the Irish situation. It gives quite a fillip to the proceedings, which are becoming decidedly dry.

Bishop Dwyer says he was simply trying to tell the people on that occasion the reason why they held St Patrick's concert. He was not born in Ireland. He had sympathies with Irish aspirations as he had with those of Belgium or anywhere else; and it was just a statement of fact that the Irish were being ill-treated because, instead of having the regular forces of England to keep order there, they had sent over some auxiliaries called 'Black-and-Tans' who were recruited from the gaols of England, and said they were committing murderous reprisals upon people, and he said that had been objected to by Mr Asquith in the House of Commons in just as severe terms as he had done, and by a great number of the fair-minded British people, including the Archbishop of Canterbury and a great number of the Church of England prelates there.

★★★

This, it is announced, is the case for the defendant.

Chapter Twenty-three

Mr Campbell approaches the bench and asks His Honour to direct the jury to find a verdict for the defendant.

His Honour replies, 'At present, I think I shall probably put to the jury the ordinary questions put in cases of malicious prosecution: did the defendant take reasonable care to inform himself of the true facts of the case; and did he honestly believe the facts he submitted to the magistrate? It is a question I can be set right upon on appeal, and I think it better to take the opinion of the jury.'

'If a Court of Appeal comes to the conclusion that Your Honour had not discharged a duty, which primarily devolved upon you, there could be no other result than that a new trial must be granted.' Mr Campbell says.

'I want to avoid the possibility of a new trial. By leaving the matter to the jury, it would, I think, lead to the least inconvenience and injustice.'

Mr Shand reminds me that my case hinges on malice. 'Did Bishop Dwyer desire to cause harm or suffering when he laid an information against you? Mr Campbell must move the jury into believing that the defendant had your best interests at heart when he made a sworn statement that you were insane.'

★★★

At 1 p.m. Mr Campbell addresses the jury.

'No sane mind could have seen in any of the trivial causes justification for the plaintiff leaving the convent. Nobody could suppose that her action was the result of anything but a seriously disturbed mind. Nobody could question the reality of the duty that rested upon the convent authorities. The plaintiff had entered the community within a week or a fortnight of her arrival in the state. She could not look to anyone except as a matter of charity. She left the shelter of the community as destitute of human resources as it was possible to be. She left that community making a charge so monstrously at variance with her own views that, even to her, if she were sane, there must have appeared, upon a moment's reflection, to have been reasonable ground to doubt her sanity.

'What was the inference that would be drawn from the circumstance of her flight except one to the discredit and injury of the innocent, gentle-minded and charitable women she had abandoned? It would be impossible to escape the suspicion that, were she perfectly sane, the sisters in the community were indescribable in their violence. Yet the court knew, so far as any coherent idea could be extracted from her belief as to the character of the members of the community, that she had no other feeling than that they were actuated by feelings of kindness and affection towards her.

'No one but herself was responsible for her sanity ever being questioned, and she got a vindication against her self-imputation, and she sought to put upon this innocent community the damnable charge of having meditated, and taken a step towards, the commission of murder.

'How did Mr Barton come into the case? The Thompsons were not called, and we were unable to get first hand what their view of her condition was, and what purpose was intended when she was taken away on the Sunday night.

'I put it to you,' Mr Campbell proceeds, 'that the circumstances were of a kind which might prove useful, at all events, acceptable, to a certain body who are notorious for having a traditional enmity against Catholic institutions and the Catholic Church. There could be no other reason for calling in Mr Barton except that the plaintiff's story might become an instrument which could be used to the injury of the convent at Wagga, and, ultimately, against the church with which the convent was associated. If there was nothing but justice intended in Mr Barton's advocacy of the plaintiff's cause, the jurymen could ask themselves why all this mysterious flitting to and fro at night.

'It is unfortunately true that the minds of some men are not free from the poison of sectarianism. Most people feel ashamed at the thought that there is in our midst a traditional enmity between two great sections of our people. It was apparently inherited; derived from, and had its beginnings in historical events and, up to this day, it has not ceased to influence the minds of men. And is so bitter and so potent that I do not think it is dealing in the language of extravagance to say that it obscures reason and confounds their judgement upon every subject that comes within its influence. I may say, with regard to this particular element, that it is a curious, as well as a deplorable fact that this traditional enmity is associated with religion, the fundamental principle of which is brotherhood – love for all our fellow men.

'I know you are capable of rising above the influence of prejudice and that you will deal with this matter judicially. My only desire is that you do strict justice, based on an impartial analysis of the evidence. I submit that there is not a scintilla of evidence to justify the charge.'

Mr Campbell moves closer to the four jurors. Minutes tick by as he holds them in his gaze. 'The first thing you, the jury, will have to ask is, in what respect did the Bishop fail to take care? The Bishop could only have omitted to take care if it appeared there was something he did not do, which might have been done, and which it was his duty to do at the time. The plaintiff disappeared in her nightgown and bare feet on a winter's night, after sitting down amicably with Mother Clare and the sisters, and having refreshment. Two months before, the plaintiff had expressed herself to the Bishop as perfectly contented. It was well known that persons suffering from delusion of insanity could go about and impress people with a sense of their perfect sanity.

'In the proper discharge of his duty towards the plaintiff, what was the next step for the Bishop to take? Obviously, to try and see her. This he tried to do, and went in compliance with the invitation contained in the letter written by her. He went to see the plaintiff with a letter written to her and one written to the Thompsons. This letter was one of the utmost correctness, and served the purpose of interpreting the Bishop's own belief in regard to the circumstances of the plaintiff's disappearance. Clearly, the Bishop, on whom responsibility for the community rested, obviously considered that, monstrous as her own explanation of what happened at the convent was, her hallucination was but temporary, and that it was desirable she should be reassured as to the feeling of the sisters and himself towards her. Though the Bishop wrote to the plaintiff at this time and enclosed a copy of the letter sent to the Thompsons, the evidence was that neither the letter nor the enclosure had been given to her.

'We know that the plaintiff was secretly removed from Wagga. The shifty proceedings in connection with this matter, the unnecessary lying and furtive deception by the Thompsons – what impression must it all have conveyed to the mind of the Bishop, inspired by the anxieties he had expressed in his letter to the Thompsons? Could he possibly come to the conclusion that the Thompsons were the proper custody in which to have the plaintiff in her supposed mental condition? Could he suppose that he would be discharging his duty if he left the plaintiff to people who were occupied in practising deception and callously lying in the way they had done – people who could not be supposed to have any wish to restore her mental condition? Would it be possible for the Bishop to suppose that, if she had this delusion, of which she had given to him overwhelming evidence in her own handwriting, the Thompsons were likely to desire to cure it?

'There had never been a moment when it was made possible for him to see her and explain that neither himself nor the Mother Superior took a serious view of her escapade. Who prevented him having that opportunity? The Thompsons and Barton and nobody else.'

***

I want to stand up and shout, 'The Bishop is on trial here – not the Thompsons, nor Mr Barton. Their sympathy and protection helped me escape the life I could no longer endure.'

Mr Campbell continues. 'The plaintiff's counsel suggests that the Bishop should have seen Doctor Tivey, but he knew that he could have got nothing more than a restatement from him. So far as medical opinion went, he was entitled to pay more regard to the opinion of Doctor Leahy, who had known the plaintiff for years, rather than the view of one who had seen her for a few minutes only.

'The Bishop had a duty to perform and had to satisfy himself that she had freedom of action and control of her own fortunes and destiny. It was imperative that she should be seen in order that her condition should be ascertained. Was the Bishop slack in that respect, or was there any indication of his failure in that direction? No, the fact was he used all the means at his disposal; the police were instructed to keep a look out for the girl.

'The girl has told her story, which was one of self-devotion and self-abnegation. She has said further that she had received nothing but kindness and sympathy. She has had the opportunity of saying anything she knew, and she has the benefit of any prompting that counsel could give her.

'On the plaintiff's evidence alone the defendant has shown that he had taken every means to inform himself of the facts, and that nothing that he could have done would have produced a different result.'

The jury is bearing up bravely, showing commendable interest in what is going forward. No doubt the solace of two guineas a day has something to do with it.

Mr Campbell continues. 'The question of whether the defendant honestly believed in the truth of the matter laid before the police magistrate – it was for the plaintiff to show that. She had left the convent without material resources. She was, as he thought, in a state of delusion. He was assured she had left Thompson's house. The Bishop was entitled to suppose that she could no longer count on any help from the Thompsons, and, in the mental condition in which he supposed her to be, that she could not depend upon her own physical capacity to pay for anything she needed. There were no grounds whatsoever for the Bishop to believe that she had any material means of support available to her, either as a right or as a natural expectation.

'Coming to the question of malice. If anyone had a malicious mind it must have been the plaintiff, who had given evidence against herself, and exposed those ladies with whom she had been in sympathetic and affectionate intercourse for years to the base suspicion of having done something that justified her desperate act. But I need not labour this question of malice. The case is destitute of any evidence upon which to rest any reasonable suggestion of the baseness of a wicked mind, seeking for some purpose, opposed to the plaintiff's interests, acting without sense of duty to the plaintiff, but for nefarious purposes, which cannot be indicated with definiteness because they are so nebulous. Finally, you have to consider that, having the information to be used for the purpose of getting the order, the defendant submits it to such persons as the Inspector General of police and to the Solicitor General, asking them what they think he should do, and apparently accepts their advice. Were they in the conspiracy, too? Were they inspired by the malice which is supposed to have moved the defendant? If not, how can the Bishop have been so inspired? Could he have done anything else?

'Supposing he had let the matter drop, taking no action at all in the prosecution of his solemn duty in relation to this unfortunate young woman, would not the accusation then have been: Here is an institution, which assumes the duty of protecting people brought together for purposes of the church, and of religion – people who are necessarily deprived of those human associations that constitute the comfort of others, who live lives sworn to poverty and to self-denial. On the other hand, here is a member of that community who has given twelve years of devoted service to the institution and the faith, flying from the convent under circumstances which indicate that her mind had become unhinged – yet the church and the convent are callously indifferent to her fate. They let her go, leave her in the care of people hostile to the faith of the institution, and in the end she is turned out stricken in mind and incapable.

'They have the effrontery to come here and say, on the evidence in this case, that no reasonable man could have entertained the belief that the Bishop, either as to her mental condition or as to her means of support, did not believe what anyone else would be entitled to believe – what the Inspector General believed, what the Solicitor General believed, what the magistrate believed, what Doctor Leahy believed, and what everyone who exercised an impartial judgment upon the facts would believe. As you cannot but be aware that there is more than the mere satisfaction of the plaintiff's complaint involved here; that there are wider issues. I ask you to deal with this case judicially on the evidence, and if you do that the Bishop may rest assured of a not guilty verdict.'

Mr Campbell closes his book of notes from which he has been speaking and pointing towards me along with my counsel, he raises his voice, repeating his words. 'They have the effrontery to come here …' Shaking his head, he throws down his notebook and apologizes for delving into detail. 'I don't want to labour the matter any longer.'

Chapter Twenty-four

M r Shand rises.

'You have been treated to a five-hour address by my friend who has endeavoured to obtrude the issue of sectarianism, and leaves the impression that, whilst he has not been responsible for it, *I* have – yet all the time it is trailing behind his coat. When I opened my case, I deliberately avoided the question of sectarianism. Now, however, my friend has brought in this charge.

'Animated, no doubt, by the gentleman instructing him, he implies that we gambled on getting a jury of Orangemen, who may be such perverts that they will callously disregard the sanctity of their oath in the interests of one of the parties. I am going to show that the Bishop never had any reasonable cause to think the plaintiff was insane.

'Mr Campbell suggests in his address that there is something deep behind this action – that the people who seem anathema to him have a deep design in this action being brought. What do we know about them? We know they had exercised the greatest kindness to this girl while she had been under their care and protection. They had not attempted to influence her in her religious belief. I hope the day is far distant when a person who comes in distress to anyone, whether Protestant or otherwise, would be turned adrift because she was of the opposite faith. And, if this girl's fears were real, there was only one way in which she could avoid being taken back to the convent, and that was by getting the protection of a body, if not as powerful as the church, at any rate, able to make its view and its influence felt.

'As far as the girl is concerned, she consulted her solicitor and instructed him to write for an apology. All she wanted from the Bishop was an expression of public sorrow that he had put the law in motion in the way he had done, and caused her the indignity that she suffered. But the Bishop, proud in his arrogance, said he wouldn't do it. One of the most material incidents in this case shows the real disposition of the Bishop – what his beliefs were and what his object was.

'On the question of malice,' Mr Shand says, 'malice does not consist in personal ill will, but in acting with an illegal motive. If a man puts the law in motion – a law, which is designed for a particular purpose – and he puts it into operation for another purpose, then that is evidence of malice. That is the class of malice that I propose to deal with in order to satisfy you, the jury, that, in the scales of justice, the evidence has been weighed down in the plaintiff's favour.

'The plaintiff had been attended for trifling ailments which did not necessitate her being relieved from her duties. Up to the time she left the convent she was never the subject of watchfulness, nor was any alteration made in her daily routine. The only thing they knew, and that was from her own lips, was that she was suffering from weakness.

'It is very important that you should know what was in the mind of the defendant, and what was in the mind of the plaintiff, and to know what each of them thought of the seriousness of the step the girl took. That she regarded it as a serious matter was beyond question; that he regarded it as a serious matter was also beyond question. Sister Brendan, who was the plaintiff's friend, had admitted that she regarded the plaintiff's action as disgracing the plaintiff and the convent.

'What was the position of the plaintiff? She had committed the most grievous sin that anyone in her position could commit; done something that would call down upon her the wrath of the other nuns, and for which the Bishop had power to coerce her with penalties. She was ordered to bed and given a dose of medicine. What was in it, we do not know. That it was poison, I do not suggest; but what if the sister giving it her, indignant at the disgrace brought upon the convent by the girl, wished to teach her a lesson? Whatever was done that night had stamped itself indelibly upon the girl's mind, coming back as she did knowing she had done wrong, fearing coercion, and not knowing what would happen to her. Whatever was done might have been with the best intentions from a religious point of view, but from a humanitarian point of view was one of the most serious possible towards one who must have been in a semi-hysterical condition.

'She knew she would have no liberty were she to be taken back, no access to the outside world. And, knowing this, she made her provisions accordingly to prevent such an eventuality. Her whole idea was to get away from Wagga, the point of immediate danger to her, and obtain in obscurity that protection her condition demanded. It had, of course, been wrong for the Thompsons to deny that she was not at their house. It has been suggested that the Thompsons knew she was mad, and that this was the reason they were not called as witnesses. It was, however, a very singular thing to find reputable people, for the sake of notoriety, voluntarily taking a person they believed to be insane into their home, caring for her, and then sending her to a sister. The Thompsons have not been called because the plaintiff's case did not require that their comfort should be disturbed, and there was ample evidence without theirs to show her movements.

'We have questioned all these people who say that Sister Liguori was sane, including Mrs Howell, who saw her and conversed with her within a few days of the time she left the convent. There is no suggestion of insanity, except this one thing, that the plaintiff formed an exaggerated idea of some physical circumstance that occurred on her return to the convent the first time. That in itself was such as to provoke a lively fear that some serious consequence was going to ensue as the result of her breaking her vows.'

Mr Shand refers to Dr Tivey's evidence that he had discovered that the girl was quite normal. He was asked to convey that opinion to the convent authorities, and he did. On the other hand, Dr Leahy had admitted that he had made no notes in his attendance upon the sister prior to 24 July. There had, in fact, been a deliberate attempt to detail small symptoms – things that were treated in ordinary illnesses, in the effort to influence the jury in a way that was not justified.

'Finally, my case rests very largely upon what took place in Wagga, between the defendant, Doctor Leahy and Mr Sheekey, upon the proceedings that were sought to be taken before the magistrate there, and upon the fact that the Bishop did not disclose to the magistrate who granted the order in Sydney that those proceedings had taken place in Wagga. These are matters for your serious consideration.

'You have seen the plaintiff in the box. She has been hunted and persecuted, and has been fleeing from everybody from then until now. Do you think she is sane at present? I ask you to find a verdict for the full amount of damages claimed.'

Chapter Twenty-five

Even after ten days of deliberations, the court is again packed and the gallery overflowing up to the final minutes, with some of the crowd equipped with opera glasses. Sitting beneath a crest of *Dieu et mon droit* (God and my right), Justice Ferguson is ready to begin his summing up as the court is called to order.

His Honour, referring to my arrest and being taken to the Reception House, directs his words to the jury. 'It was no doubt a very great indignity for any person to be subjected to. If it were done without any improper conduct on the part of the defendant, then it is an indignity for which the plaintiff has no redress. If the defendant acted lawfully and without malice, and with reasonable and probable cause, then, even if he were absolutely mistaken, she must submit to it, and, as far as damages against her are concerned, she has no redress at all. The plaintiff's evidence said nothing whatever about any treatment of which she had to complain during all the time she was a member of the convent up to the afternoon of the 24th July. She had told the Bishop, only a few months before she left, that she was happy and contented and had no complaint to make other than she was overworked and appeared to have been hurt when she was taken away from her teaching duties and put to duties that properly belonged, as she thought, to a lay sister. She had given a sub-division of her day, a distribution of duties which left very little time for herself; but that was apparently the ordinary practice of the convent; that was the discipline to which she voluntarily submitted when she entered the order.

'Her evidence of any unkindness shown to her during the years of her stay at the convent have been conclusively repudiated, not by the contradiction of people interested, not by the balance of conflicting testimony, but by her own deliberate oath.'

My own deliberate oath! How could I discredit the whole Mount Erin community, when only a few, while professing religion, practise it so sparingly?

The four men of the jury listen intently as His Honour continues.

'Considering, as you have to do, the conduct of the defendant, you must put yourself in his position, and remember what he knew when he took the steps he did take. He made enquiries and finally he swore an information in which he said she was a person deemed to be insane and without sufficient means of support. The questions for you and me are:

'Did the defendant take reasonable care to inform himself as to the true facts of the case? Did he honestly believe the case that he laid before the magistrate?

'Unless the plaintiff has satisfied you that you should answer one or other of these questions in the negative, then the defendant is entitled to a verdict. I am also going to ask you a further question, which only becomes material if you find against him on one of the other questions. Was he actuated by malice?'

The jury retires. Three p.m. ... four p.m. ... four-thirty p.m. ... and the jury is still out.

'What is keeping them?' whispers Mrs Touchell, checking the time and continually watching the door through which they withdrew.

A few minutes later the court crier announces that the court is adjourned until eight p.m. The courtroom empties and Mr Shand explains the position. 'The jury has to either agree unanimously on a verdict or deliberate for the full six hours, at the expiration of which time the judge is empowered to accept a majority verdict ... but not until then. In the event of a complete disagreement, the case will be put down for rehearing.'

The queues outside the court are the longest they have ever been. A special police force patrols the vicinity and the excitement is palpable. Commotion erupts when the clerk strides into the courtroom at 9.42 pm, followed by the jury. Those who had left, scurry back to their seats just in time to hear the order for 'Silence in court'.

'Have you agreed, gentlemen, upon a verdict?' His Honour asks.

'Yes, Your Honour,' answers the foreman.

'Are you unanimous or by a majority?'

'A majority on the first two questions and unanimous in the last.'

The foreman hands the judge the paper on which His Honour had written the questions for consideration and on which they have recorded their answers. Judge Ferguson shows no emotion as he glances at the document. In the hushed courtroom, His Honour's words can be heard clearly.

'Did the defendant take reasonable care to inform himself as to the true facts of the case?' he asks the foreman.

'The answer is "No", Your Honour.'

'Did the defendant honestly believe the case which he laid before the magistrate?'

'No, Your Honour.'

Mrs Touchell grabs my arm. 'Does this mean we have won, Brigid?'

Holding our breath we wait for the final reply.

'Was the defendant actuated by malice?'

'Again, the answer is "No", Your Honour.'

Spontaneous gasps erupt from the gallery and the clerk calls for immediate silence.

'How do you find, gentlemen: for the plaintiff, or for the defendant?'

'By direction – for the defendant.'

The worn wooden benches at the back of the court burst into scenes of jubilation. Order is quickly restored as His Honour thanks the jury for the very great care they have taken and apologizes for keeping them so long over the case.

The Bishop's face is masked in smug satisfaction as his counsel congratulates him. In turn, he thanks them for providing such a strong defence.

As he walks triumphant to the door, people shout and rush towards him, patting him on the back and shaking his hand. He leaves the courtroom jubilant as he joins the great sea of people outside who are still cheering wildly at the verdict.

Remaining in my seat, I bury my head in my hands. Mr Barton and the Reverend Touchell make their way towards me, offering their sympathy. 'I am relieved it is over,' I say, rising to leave.

Mr Shand escorts us from the courtroom and Mrs Touchell asks him to explain the verdict.

'Malice is a necessary legal element of the case. Despite the other two answers, the judge is bound to enter judgement for Bishop Dwyer,' he explains. 'Judge Ferguson has delivered many verdicts during his time, but I'm sure never one which has given such dissatisfaction as that recorded upon the findings of a majority of this jury.'

'I am happy with the verdict,' I tell him. 'They found that Bishop Dwyer did not take the trouble to verify his facts before he swore an information that I was "deemed to be insane and without means of support" and, what is much more striking, is that he avoided telling the truth in order to attain his desire that I should be arrested under the Lunacy Laws.'

'You had good claim for redress, but the law has directed otherwise. We could appeal?'

'I can see no good purpose to be gained by appealing. It may appear to be a victory for the Bishop but it is a victory for me, too. I wanted to be vindicated in the eyes of the world and I take the view that the answers given by the jury to the first two questions have completely vindicated me.'

Mrs Touchell links my arm and on Wednesday, 13 July 1921, we leave the Supreme Court behind knowing *The Liguori Case* will not be forgotten for a long time.

Chapter Twenty-six

Newspapers offering daily updates on the story continue to hold the public's attention, while articles and letters to the editor debate the verdict. The *Sydney Morning Herald* reports Bishop Dwyer's jubilant return to Wagga Wagga, where hundreds of residents listened to his homecoming speech.

> *'Since this day twelve months ago I have not had anything but the sincerest sympathy for the girl who has been the cause of all the trouble. I say that she has not been allowed to use her own mind. She has been a mere automaton, doing what a certain lot of people forced her to do, and yet, in spite of all this, she has not said a word to discredit the Mount Erin community. That is the best of all, and has won the admiration of greater and broad-minded Protestants. No doubt in the beginning we had a trying time, but what I wanted to know was whether the girl was sane enough in order to know whether or not she wanted to be out of the convent. Some people here undertook to hide her away from us for some reason. A letter was written to them, and this was not done in haste, but on legal advice, but it was not replied to, and the judge said that no letter could have better deserved a reply. It showed that the people did not want to answer it, and showed that those who had her did not want to give her up, but to use her to try to break up the Catholic Church.'*

The *Sydney Morning Herald* also reports that the bishop attended a large meeting of Roman Catholics at St Joseph's Hall, Temora, bringing in donations amounting to £3,500.

When I was appointed as Bishop three years ago I would have much preferred to remain at Temora as parish priest. If my future in office is to be as strenuous as the past I would prefer to get out. The money collected will be used to defray the expenses in the recent case and the balance will be devoted to the completion of the Wagga Cathedral. Miss Partridge placed me in the unpleasant position of a defendant in court but I hold no animosity towards her. If I could take her out of the prison she is now in, I would do so, and give her back to her brother. She is more a prisoner now than ever she was before. I have the greatest sympathy for her and hope to see the day she will get out of where she is now as easily as she got out of the convent. I was entitled to have my costs in the case paid by those behind Miss Partridge, but they would not do so. The verdict entitled me to costs, but I have to pay my own. This is another sample of their British fair play. The plaintiff was without money when she left the convent so I could not get anything from her. Those standing behind her were not manly enough to meet all the costs. The verdict was not so much the result of clever lawyers as of Divine Providence acting in answer to the prayers of the people. Those who wanted the convents to be open for inspection should first clean their own institutions and lives.

The *Sydney Morning Herald* prints my reply on 13 August 1921.

The Bishop says he has the greatest sympathy for me, and hopes to see the day I will get out of where I am now as easily as I got out of the convent. I am not a prisoner. I am remaining of my own free will and intend to continue to do so. I appreciate what has been done for me by so many kind friends. I believe he would like to take me from my friends and give me back to my brother. He need not trouble. I am not going. His great sympathy is of no use to me; I do not require it. I am old enough and capable to think and act for myself.

Mr Barton also makes a statement:

I deny that Miss Partridge is a prisoner. She has perfect liberty to please herself, and does so. I have no doubt that the Bishop would like to hand her over to her brother but she has a say in that. She is a woman thirty years of age, her brother is her junior by about eight years, and surely she can please herself where she will remain and the company she will keep. Only a few weeks ago, Miss Partridge was in the mountains for a holiday, and was followed. She wrote from there complaining, and asked for police protection. I, with others, have befriended Miss Partridge ever since she left the convent, and so long as she desires any protection I am prepared to defend her, as I have done in the past. The Bishop added that he was entitled to have his costs in the case. That may be so: but he can only blame himself; if he had only shown that sympathy he talks about earlier he would have saved the costs.

Chapter Twenty-seven

Hoping to finally obtain peace after the trial, I travelled to Berry for a rest with Mr Barton, his wife and his daughter. I hadn't seen Joseph for a while, but he had contacted me several times through my solicitor. He followed me to Berry, persistent in his demand that I should place myself under his care. I refused and returned to Sydney. As the months pass, the publicity surrounding *The Liguori Case* slowly fades. In early October, I receive a communication from Joseph through my solicitor, informing me he is returning to Ireland and makes a final appeal that I should return with him. Again, I refuse. On 25 October, I receive a cable supposedly from my father. All the years I had wished for a letter from my family, but this fills me with dread. It tells me to accompany Joseph back to Ireland. I suspect it is another ploy to get me away from Mr Barton and the Touchells. How can I return with him? I would never be allowed to forget the shame I have brought upon myself by escaping the chains binding me to a life of hard discipline. My sanity would have been better tested for wanting to remain in the convent, rather than wishing to escape.

We are returning from a Home Mission Festival in Sydney Town Hall, the following night. It is late – almost eleven o'clock. Mrs Touchell is holding on to my arm as we saunter along the footpath behind the Reverend Touchell and his elderly father. Turning the corner of Gray Street and Chapel Street, Mrs Touchell says, 'Look up, Brigid. The sky is lit with an array of stars. It is so peaceful.' As we reach the gate of our home, we are faced with a band of men who rush towards Mr Touchell. More men appear and we are quickly surrounded. Someone grabs hold of me and I frantically fight back, screaming and struggling to stay on my feet as I witness Mrs Touchell being pushed to the ground.

I hear my brother's voice. 'It's all right, Touchell … we don't want you.'

The Reverend Touchell breaks free from his captors and immediately tries to assist us, but before he can help, a car rushes up and screeches to a halt.

'Get in, Brigid,' my brother demands.

'I don't want to get inside.' I protest loudly before being bundled roughly into the back seat.

'Don't hurt my sister,' Joseph orders when some men jump in after me, while others leap on to the footboard as the car drives off.

The pain in my back worsens as I sit bent and squashed on Joseph's knee for over an hour. Thoughts of Mrs Touchell lying sprawled on the pavement give rise to tears. Shaken and bruised, I have difficulty understanding my brother's actions. We arrive in Ashfield and I am told we are at the home of Jack Charlton, a Justice of the Peace. Joseph pulls me from the car and leads me inside. I am made to sit down at a table where a pen and some paper have been placed. 'I'm going to see that no one meddles with you.' Joseph begins writing and when he is finished, he pushes it in front of me. It reads, 'I wish to remain with my brother and wish to go with him in the future. I have voluntarily forsaken the persons with whom I have recently lived.'

'Sign it!' he orders.

'How can you do this to me, Joseph?'

'Just sign it or there will be consequences.' His sharp breath cuts through me as he bends over and watches me put my name to it.

'Now write, "Signed this 26th day of October 1921". We'll get this statement put in *The Sun* tomorrow and I'll make you a copy to keep. I want you to remain with me for a week or longer just to let you see that the church has no designs on you.'

Joseph tells me that he had men watching Barton in Berry and the Touchells' place in Kogarah and had been carefully planning this kidnapping for weeks.

I am still anxious about Mrs Touchell and need to know if she is all right. I ask can I telephone her to let her know I am unharmed, but I am refused. Joseph and I argue through the night. He uses every tactic to win me round to his way of thinking. I play along, but I must find a way to escape.

'If I am to stay in this house, I will have to have some form of amusement. Could I buy some beads at Anthony Hordern's to make things with?'

Joseph agrees.

'Do you have a pencil and paper to write down my order?'

'I don't think that is necessary,' I wonder does he realize my intention of writing a note to the assistant to call the police?

I remind him in the morning of his promise. 'Show me that I am free and let me have a day out to buy the materials I need for my hobby.'

I am elated when he decides to remain behind while one of the men, named Mr O'Callaghan, takes me into town. Before leaving, I am told to change my dress so that I won't be recognized and am provided with some clothes. Joseph wants us to take the car, but I insist we take a tram from Haberfield, secretly hoping I will meet someone who will come to my aid. Arriving in Sydney, we get off at the corner of Hunter Street and George Street.

Mr O'Callaghan leads me into a refreshment room close by. While he is ordering some soda water, I look out of the shop door and to my joy I recognize a gentleman on the other side of the road. I beckon, making signs to him, pointing to myself and then to him and then to Mr O'Callaghan. I watch in disbelief when he raises his eyebrows and suddenly walks away. I want to shout, 'Come back, Mr Roache,' as I look all around to see where he has gone.

'You're very nervous, Miss Partridge. What are you looking at?'

'I thought I saw a familiar face. Can't I say good morning to a friend if I see one?'

'Your brother and some of the other men have arranged to meet us in town later. Do you want to go to the Botanic Gardens?'

'Yes, I would like that.' On our way along Macquarie Street, a man steps from behind us and taps Mr O'Callaghan on the shoulder. I turn to see Mr Roache with another gentleman who asks, 'Who's the lady?'

'Miss Partridge,' answers Mr O'Callaghan.

'Are you a detective?' I quickly ask.

'Yes, I am.'

'Well, for the present I place myself under your protection. Don't let anyone take me away!'

The detective asks us to escort him back to Police Headquarters and I am taken to Superintendent Bannan's office. Familiar with the publicity already surrounding me, the police are wary about taking any action in the matter as they regard me a free agent. After consulting with the Inspector General, Superintendent Bannan decides not to take a statement from me until I have seen my solicitor, Mr Hill, in case of litigation. They contact Mr Hill for me.

The news I have been found quickly spreads and within a short time Mr and Mrs Touchell are at my side, along with others. I am so happy to be back among the friends I had been wrenched from. Joseph arrives at lunchtime. Pressmen, photographers and some members of the public besiege the detective's office.

I take a seat at the top of a long table beside Mr Hill, Mrs Touchell, Reverend Touchell and Mr Barton. On the other side are my brother and Mr Peter Gallagher, secretary to the Attorney General. Standing is Superintendent Bannan and many other police officials and detectives.

During a tense three-hour argument, Joseph produces the documents he forced me to sign, saying 'This is your statement, made last night.'

'It is not my statement, *you* wrote it.'

Superintendent Bannan addresses me. 'As the representative of the Inspector General it is my duty to give you what protection the law allows. I want you to understand clearly that you are free to go to whom you choose, or to wherever you desire. With whom do you wish to go?'

I stand up slowly, calmly, 'I desire to go back to the protection of Mr Hill, my solicitor. I am not going to Ireland with my brother. After what he has done, I can only say may God forgive him for his treatment of me. I have had enough worry and do not want any more.' I sit down again in my chair.

Joseph is on his feet, anger evident on his face. I cannot meet his furious eyes. 'That's all right, Brigid. Goodbye.' He strides brusquely to the door.

I am ushered into a room. Mr Hill consults with me about taking action against Joseph for his part in my kidnapping and I manifestly refuse to give evidence against him. We discuss where I am to be taken and Mr Touchell says, 'You are free to do as you wish but you are welcome to stay with us for as long as you please.' My mind is made up and we then discuss the best means of getting away without having to run the gauntlet of so many curious eyes. A car glides up to the side entrance in Phillip Street and I slip happily into the seat beside Mrs Touchell. Leaving Police Headquarters, I glimpse Joseph. Looking out of the rear window as we pass, he fixes me with a cold stare. Turning up his collar, he crosses the road and I lose sight of his outline as he disappears into the crowds on a Sydney street. Will he ever understand how difficult this has been for me? My head drops in despair as I try to make sense of it all.

'You have had a bad time of it, Brigid,' says Mrs Touchell, leaving me alone to cry on the journey back to Kogarah.

★★★

Everyone claps when I walk into the crowded kitchen where dozens of friends and neighbours are gathered. They beg me to tell them about my ordeal. 'I was not afraid during the kidnapping as I have great faith in God. But I must not forget Mr Roache, the kind businessman from Burwood, who rescued me. I had met him twice at the Strathfield Orange Orphan Homes. He was travelling by train to the city and luckily for me he had been reading the story of my kidnapping in the *Daily Telegraph*. Arriving at the Central Station, he took a tram to Hunter Street. Shortly after alighting, he saw me in the company of a tall, stout man. Would you believe it? Keeping his distance, he followed us to the refreshment room. He then hurried into the detective's office telling Superintendent Bannan that I was in the street and that I needed police protection. A detective set out immediately and caught up with us near the Botanic Gardens.'

To end such a memorable day, Mrs Touchell presents me with a cake decorated with the words *Welcome Home!*

I write to my parents informing them of the recent events and my decision to stay with the Touchells. 'Mama will understand it is better for me to remain in Australia. I don't want to cause her any more pain. If I return to The Curragh, there would be never-ending questions to answer. The worry of it could kill her.'

A short time later, Mrs Touchell reads me a telegram she has received from my sister, Lizzie. 'It is on behalf of my mother and father and all my family to thank you a little for all your kindness to our poor Brigid in her hour of need.'

Chapter Twenty-eight

I live happily with the Touchells for many years and I am often asked to relate my story at Congregational meetings whenever the Reverend Touchell changes districts. We move to the Cessnock coalfields in 1928 and to Cronulla, Sutherland in 1931 and finally settle at 34 Donald Street, Hurstville. The name Sister Liguori has long disappeared from everybody's lips and neighbours in the quiet Sydney suburb know me simply as Miss Partridge. After the death of the Reverend Touchell in 1954, interest is awakened in the story and I am contacted by *The People* magazine for an interview.

'You were the central figure in the heated public controversy of some thirty-four years ago?' the young reporter says when he comes armed with a notebook, a tape recorder and a camera.

Speaking into the microphone, I tell him that while I was in the convent I knew nothing of the world. Throughout 1919 and during the first half of 1920 I was discontented, thinking that perhaps I had no vocation and that God had not, after all, called me to do His work within an enclosed order. Being of a shy, quiet nature, I half-heartedly complained, but my complaints fell on deaf ears. I wondered would I prefer a secular life? The simplest of solutions – to ask for a dispensation – did not suggest itself. I finish my story and tell him of my continuing fears after my brother kidnapped me.

'I still have a high regard for the work nuns do,' I insist and go on to tell him that I am happiest at home with Mrs Touchell and our pets, an asthmatic fat dog called Roley, and Jessie, the cat.

Mrs Touchell and I pose for photographs and the reporter offers to accompany me on a shopping trip to take more photographs.

'I'll be back soon,' I tell Mrs Touchell.

'You know I worry you are not taking enough rest, Paddy,' she answers from the kitchen.

'We can rest when we are dead, Mike.'

I smile at the terms of endearment between two old ladies whose friendship has remained constant for over forty years. We became inseparable after the kidnapping, but since the Reverend Touchell's death, Mrs Touchell is more protective. I tuck my grey, wiry hair into a knot at the back of my head, put on a navy broad-brimmed hat, and pull a brown coat over my faded grey ankle-length dress. Finally, I slip my feet into a comfortable pair of black walking brogues before catching the bus with the reporter to the shopping centre. The candied smell of sugary confectionery tempts us into a sweet shop. Some children are trying to decide if they want chocolate caramels or ice cream as they count their pennies. Searching through my tattered purse for a few loose coins, I help them make up their minds. We talk about the delights of ice cream as they lick their frozen treats.

My day in the spotlight is over and a few weeks later my interview appears in *The People* magazine in August 1954, *The Nun who Ran Away*. For a while, I am stopped in the street, but things soon settle down again.

★★★

I am in the Commonwealth Bank one day and, stepping back from the counter, I almost collide with a slim, grey-haired lady standing in the queue behind me.

'H-h-hello ... Sister ... I mean ...' she says.

'Where do I know you from?'

'Wagga!'

Her dark brown eyes trigger a memory. 'Was it in the playground?'

'Yes.'

I take her to the side where we can talk quietly.

'What is your name?'

'I was Sheila Byrne, but I am married now to William Tearle. We live here in Hurstville with our son.'

'Ah, how could I forget young Sheila Byrne? You often brought me flowers. Do you still keep in touch with Mount Erin?'

'Yes, I do.'

Cut off for so long from communication with the convent, I am eager to learn of the nuns. 'Do you have any news of Sister Kostka? She treated me like her own sister and took me cups of tea when I was ill. And Sister Raphael? She had such beautiful eyes. And Sister de Sales? She had lovely rosy cheeks.' My questions go on and on until I can name no more. Finally, I ask her to give each and all of them my love. I frequently meet Sheila 'up the street' and we always stop for a chat.

Some days I catch a bus to St Michael's Church in Hurstville. The bus stop is directly beside the Church and when I alight, I cross the road to a wooden bench opposite and sit contemplating the open doors of the brick building. I have not been inside a Roman Catholic Church for thirty years.

Sheila has asked Father Peter Morrissey, the curate in Hurstville, to pay me a visit and Mrs Touchell, who is now almost ninety years old, is intrigued to be answering the door to the young Catholic priest. He finds me settled in a chair in the corner of the dining room, a black knitted shawl thrown across my shoulders. Jessie, our half-Persian cat, lies curled in a brown mottled ball on a spare chair beside me. Father Morrissey looks around at the faded photographs hanging on the streaked wallpaper of people and old churches belonging to another era. I see him looking at the cluttered tables and surfaces littered with stacks of yellowing newspapers preserving the bitter drama of 1920 and the court case of 1921. He glances at the pair of shiny glass rosary beads held between my fingers.

'I hope I am not disturbing you, Miss Partridge.' He removes the threadbare cushion from behind him, and something falls to the floor. He bends down to pick up the single piece of cardboard with seven photographs pasted on to it.

'Is this your family in Ireland?'

'Yes, Father. I was not allowed to have photographs in the convent. The day I left I vowed to have a family album. My brother

Joseph gave me those. He's the one at the bottom right-hand corner, beside me.' The memory of Joseph causes a tear to roll down my cheek. How often have I prayed for the rift between us to be healed?

'Brigid … can I call you Brigid?'

'Of course, Father.'

'Would you like me to hear your confession and receive Holy Communion?'

'Yes … I would like that.'

Mrs Touchell sings out from the kitchen. 'Don't take any notice of him, Paddy.'

Father Morrissey says he should not have troubled me and when Mrs Touchell shows him to the door, I hear her say, 'I could arrange to get you a wife if you want one.' For better or worse, Father Morrissey declines the offer.

I look forward to seeing the young priest again and when he calls several weeks later, Mrs Touchell goes off to make a cup of tea, leaving us alone and we talk about the young people in the parish. He is moved away from Hurstville shortly afterwards and I miss his visits.

A neighbour, Mrs Mulholland, helps us in the house and with shopping, but when she is admitted to hospital, we are no longer able to look after ourselves. We leave our Donald Street home in November 1962 when the doctor admits us to North Ryde Hospital. We are then transferred to Rydalmere Psychiatric Hospital, which is basically a nursing home. Mrs Touchell's health is deteriorating and in early September 1963 she is moved to a private room.

I am alone in the ward when the matron appears. She pulls up a chair beside me. I stare blankly waiting to hear what is written on her face.

'Mrs Touchell died in her sleep a short time ago.' The news is whispered, but it doesn't soften the blow. When the matron leaves the ward, I get up and move towards the empty bed where my dearest friend once slept. I sit down heavily, gripping the blankets and twisting them into a knot. How can I stop this pain? I find a pocket of air and digging deep into the memories of forty-three years of friendship, I remain there drenching the bed with tears. The pain subsides when I fall asleep but as soon as I wake grief overpowers me again. Time passes unnoticed until the gentle ticking of my watch sparks a memory.

'It is God's fingers tapping the glass, like a heartbeat, reminding us how precious each second of our life is.'

★★★

Several days later, a familiar voice drifts from the corridor, 'I read of Mrs Touchell's death in the paper.'

'Miss Partridge never has visitors and we often find her slumped over the bed of her departed friend. We worried she had no one. How do you know her?'

'Miss Partridge was once a nun in a country convent.'

'You can tell … every inch of her is so refined.' The Matron's reply makes me smile. If only she knew.

The Matron sets me in my chair, making me comfortable with a pillow behind my back to receive my visitor.

'Do you still have your rosary beads?' Sheila Tearle asks.

'No, I don't need them, I have my ten fingers,' I say, holding up my hands. 'Would you like to see the Catholic chaplain?'

'I don't need to go to confession. I can say an Act of Contrition and I'll be all right.' I fold my hands back down on to my lap, a habit I cannot break.

Sheila often visits and informs me that a new curate in Hurstville, Father Edward Wilkinson, has visited Ireland and has been in contact with Joseph. Sheila sees me struggling to sit up when I hear my brother's name and props me up straighter. How often have I prayed for news of him?

'Father Wilkinson asked me to pass this on to you.' Sheila says.

It is almost sixty years since I held my girlhood prayer book. It is easy to remember the naive seventeen-year-old who had high ideals. How life changes our perception of things! Sheila tells me that Father Wilkinson also wanted to pass on some words from Joseph.

'As far as I can judge my own sister, I believe she is innocent in the sight of God of any wrong. But she was not, at the time of the incident in Wagga, capable of forming a sensible judgment – I think that is quite clear. Her fears at the time and for the past forty years have been kept alive and I doubt if she is more capable today of a sound judgment. But she is not insane and never was. She was ever praying and closer to God than I could ever hope to be.'

Joseph has also written me a letter and I ask Sheila to read it out as I need new glasses '... *and I made a visit to the Holy Land and to Calvary where I prayed for you, Bride.*' Many tears have been shed, sorrow, pain, regret, and now the quiet tears of joy.

In 1966, Father Morrissey returns to Sydney and in early December he accompanies Sheila to Rydalmere. I am in a side room that is much brighter and more cheerful than the large ward, with its institutional walls and windows fitted with steel grilles that keep the light out. Now, I can see the blue sky from where I lie. The nurse has brushed my hair back, and it flutters in the cool breeze blowing from the fan beside my bed. I am happy to see the young priest again and he gives me a blessing. Sheila holds a cup of water to my mouth, pleading that I take a few sips to moisten my dry lips. Tiring easily, sleep carries me back to the playground in Wagga. Children are running towards me. I want to say goodbye to them and stretch out my hand. Sheila reaches me first, pressing her small hand into mine.

Chapter Twenty-nine

December 1966

Sheila Tearle's testimony

Sheila clasps Brigid's hand into hers. Those hard-worked hands, now at rest, remind her of her school days. The children loved the young Irish nun who looked after them on the playground. As soon as the gate opened, they dashed forward each hoping to be the first to reach her. When she disappeared, they tried to solve the mystery. They wondered was she ill and Sheila had checked behind the water tanks for the flowers she had hidden there. The cream blooms lay limp and unclaimed. When the children learned that Sister Liguori had run away during the night, Sheila was bitterly disappointed that she never got the holy card she was promised. The notoriety Sister Liguori had gained through the newspapers reporting the incident led to an extraordinary interest in the Court Case in Sydney. Even as a young girl, Sheila was aware of the sectarianism it aroused, dividing the people of Wagga.

Nearly four decades would pass before she would see Sister Liguori again. Waiting to be served in the Commonwealth Bank in Hurstville, she immediately recognized the tall woman wearing a dark blue wide-brimmed hat standing at the counter in front of her. She hadn't lost her nun-like manner. Sheila had startled her when she said hello, and then the friendly smile appeared, spreading its warmth in a greeting back. Sister Liguori had enquired after the nuns at Mount Erin with such affection that Sheila knew she genuinely cared for each of them. It was hard not to notice how the strain of her troubled and dramatic life had taken its toll. Had she ever regretted her actions? Suddenly, Brigid's grip tightens and the rhythm of her breathing changes. Sheila asks the matron to contact her if her condition worsens.

A phone call comes from Rydalmere two days later: 'Miss Partridge passed away on Sunday night.'

'Thank you, Matron. Do you know what the burial arrangements are?'

'Miss Partridge's dying wish was to be buried beside her friend, Mrs Touchell, but I will ring you as soon as I have any further information.'

When the Matron rings back, she tells Sheila, 'I have checked our records and Miss Partridge cannot be buried beside Mrs Touchell.'

'Why is that?'

'Mrs Touchell was cremated.'

'What will happen now?'

'Well, Miss Partridge has no known relatives in Australia and as her only regular visitor, Mrs Tearle, you are entitled to take possession of the body.'

Sheila tightens her hold on the telephone, overcome at being charged with such responsibility, 'How can I take possession of the body? Miss Partridge has a brother in Ireland! I will make some enquiries and keep you informed.' As soon as Sheila replaces the receiver, she rings Father Tom Dunlea, her parish priest in Hurstville, who telephones Joseph Partridge in Ireland. He requests a Catholic burial for his sister. This is quickly ruled out when Rydalmere rings Sheila informing her that instructions have been left with W. H. Timmins, Funeral Director of Timmins Parlour in Paramatta, for Brigid's burial. They do not know, at this stage, when the funeral will be and tell Sheila they will ring her. Days go by and there is no phone call. Sheila learns it will be 'fitted in' when the opportunity presents itself. Sheila's fear is that Brigid will be accorded a pauper's funeral and asks Father Morrissey to do the funeral. Not wishing to start another sectarian war, he declines but arranges for the St Vincent de Paul Society to bury her wherever required. Eventually, Sheila is assured that Mrs Touchell has left money for a Congregationalist burial to be performed and is notified that the funeral will take place on Friday, 16 December.

Sheila picks a colourful bunch of red and yellow gardenia from her garden before leaving Hurstville to be at Timmins Parlour at Parramatta for 9.15 a.m. She is dressed in a matching black skirt and jacket and wears her best black court shoes. All is quiet when she arrives. She is concerned that no one is there, and rings Father Morrissey who is at Five Dock. While she is talking, a tall man appears – the Reverend Gordon Riley, the Congregational minister who is to conduct the funeral. But when Sheila asks what is the hold-up, she is told they have to wait for the coach to come back. It is at another funeral.

'Please don't mind me. I can travel on the hearse with the minister,' Sheila says. But the coach has been 'provided for' and she is asked to wait. It eventually arrives and Sheila is ushered into it.

Brigid is to be buried in a graveyard in a Sydney suburb. Driving through the main entrance of Rookwood, Sheila looks ahead to hundreds of acres divided into religious sections where stone-faced angels watch over almost a million interments. They follow the road around to the independent section, stopping at a corner. The plain wooden coffin is removed from the hearse and carried to the graveside. Mr Riley recites a few prayers and Sheila, the only mourner, joins in the simple ceremony as the coffin is gently lowered into the ground. She waits for the gravediggers to refill the grave before setting her gardenia on top, remembering how the small gift of flowers brought an instant flush of excitement to the young nun's cheeks.

It is late afternoon when Sheila arrives home, tired and relieved to slip her aching feet into a pair of comfortable brown slippers. She makes a pot of tea and sits down with her thoughts. Last Sunday, she attended Mass at St Michael's Church in Hurstville and Father Tom Dunlea had read out the name Brigid Mary Partridge in the list of

Masses for the dead. The announcement hadn't caused the slightest ripple. Not even a gesture of surprise, a questioning glance, or a remark of any kind. How different the reaction would have been had the name Sister Liguori been read out!

Sheila remembers the post. It is almost Christmas and the letterbox is full of cards. Going through them slowly, a particular one jumps out. From a friend in a religious order, it is a holy card trimmed with paper lace. She sinks deep into her chair at the haunting coincidence of a promise made forty-six years before.

Many years later

The sun is high in a cloudless sky over the city of Sydney and Sheila, trying to escape the suffocating heat, quickly turns the corner into Macquarie Place. She climbs up the steps to the Mitchell Library, past the tall columns supporting the grand entrance, and through the towering bronze doors into the Reading Rooms. She will shelter here for a while and welcomes the cool breeze blowing from the electric fans. Searching the overloaded shelves, she chooses a book on local history and sits down at a large wooden table. She looks up when a Christian Brother sits beside her. 'I have a keen interest in local history, too,' he whispers, setting an old copy of *The People* magazine down in front of him. It is dated August 1954. Turning the pages slowly, an article on page 5 captures his interest, *The Nun Who Ran Away*.

When he has finished reading, Sheila tells him, 'I knew Sister Liguori when she was in the convent at Wagga; she died in 1966.'

'Do you know where she is buried? I would like to visit her grave.'

'It's not far from here, Brother. I could take you, if you like.'

'Well, there's no time like the present.' He tucks his small black prayer book under his arm. On the way to catch a bus to the cemetery, they talk about the troubled young Irish nun who lost faith.

'My memory is not so good,' Sheila says as they pass crumbling headstones and the Christian Brother's skinny fingers wipe chalky dust away to read the faded inscriptions.

'There are acres upon acres of graves,' he says. The dull thud of a spade alerts them to a mound of freshly dug earth, and, looking into the blackness of a gaping hole, they seek guidance from the gravedigger below.

'You're maybe looking for the independent section. Call at the office and they will give you the grave number.'

They pick their way along a moss-covered path where wilting wreaths lie scattered among trailing brambles that snatch at their clothes like claws pouncing on prey. They find the grave in a deserted corner. It is unmarked and forgotten beneath a mass of tangled overgrowth. Dropping to his knees, Brother Chanel pulls distractedly at some of the loose weeds. They work tirelessly together and when they have cleared the small plot, they remain on their knees as the Christian Brother reads a passage from his prayer book, finishing with a blessing. He rises to straighten his aching back and brushing dry earth from his clothes, he tells Sheila, 'Brigid Partridge should be better remembered,' before going in search of the Head Groundsman.

While he is gone, Sheila is lured into a florist's booth where fresh flowers are bunched together in buckets on tiered stands. She asks the young assistant to make up a bouquet of cream roses. Back at the graveside, she hears Brother Chanel ask for permission to place a marker on Brigid's grave and the Head Groundsman refuses.

'You are not a relation. It would not be allowed.'

Brother Chanel urges him to listen to the young nun's story, saying finally, 'She did what many were afraid to do!'

Relenting, the Head Groundsman says, 'Brother, you have my permission, but you and I have not had this conversation.'

Sheila sets the cream roses onto the grave, their fragrance filling the evening air as she tells the Christian Brother that the years will never blot the memory of how she smuggled flowers into school for her favourite nun.

Brother Chanel returns the following day with a metal plaque attached to a piece of grey polished stone and places it at her feet.

Brigid Mary Partridge
Died 4 December 1966
RIP